Daniel Varè was born in 1880, the son
of an Italian nationalist exiled with
Mazzini by the Austrian regime.
Although he was brought up in
Scotland where his parents met, Daniel
Varè returned to Italy when he was
still young and entered that country's
diplomatic service. He served in
Vienna, Geneva, Copenhagen and
Luxembourg. However, his chief
posting was in Peking where he
arrived in 1908 and where he served
for twelve years. During his time there
he saw the overthrow of the Manchu
dynasty, the country swept by civil
war and the effects of the Russian
Revolution and the First World War as
exiles fled into China from abroad.
Many of these experiences became the
subject matter of his novels and tales.

Daniel Varè left the diplomatic service
in 1932 in order to devote himself to
writing. Many of his books were
published in both Italian and English.

The Maker of Heavenly Trousers was
first published in 1935 and was
reprinted several times: it was
followed soon after by its two sequels
The Gate of Happy Sparrows and The
Temple of Costly Experience, and by
the author's autobiography, The
Laughing Diplomat in 1938. Daniel
Varè died in 1956.

Also by Daniel Varè
THE MAKER OF HEAVENLY TROUSERS
and published by Black Swan

The Gate of Happy Sparrows

Daniel Varè

BLACK SWAN

THE GATE OF HAPPY SPARROWS

A BLACK SWAN BOOK 0 552 99241 0

Originally published in Great Britain by
Methuen and Co. Ltd.

PRINTING HISTORY

Methuen edition published 1937
Black Swan edition published 1987

This book is set in 11/12 pt Mallard
by Colset Private Limited, Singapore.

Black Swan Books are published by
Transworld Publishers Ltd., 61 – 63
Uxbridge Road, Ealing, London W5 5SA, in
Australia by Transworld Publishers
(Australia) Pty. Ltd., 15 – 23 Helles Avenue,
Moorebank, NSW 2170, and in New Zealand
by Transworld Publishers (N.Z.) Ltd., Cnr.
Moselle and Waipareira Avenues,
Henderson, Auckland.

Made and printed in Great Britain by
The Guernsey Press Co. Ltd., Guernsey, Channel Islands.

TO
J.O.P. BLAND

Contents

The story "A Question of Etiquette," which forms chapter II of this book, was originally published in Harper's Magazine, New York, to the Editor of which the Author's thanks are due for permission to reprint.

Preface

Since I wrote about us all in *The Maker of Heavenly Trousers*, there has been an addition to our family. We call him Little Chink.

He was born in November, on the Fourteenth Day of the Tenth Moon, and he is now two years old.

While he was on the way, and even before, the Family of the Five Virtues (they are my Chinese servants) nearly drove us crazy with all sorts of charms and superstitions intended to ensure the continuity of the family tree. I refused to allow them to keep a naked sword under our mattress, but I had to put up with peanuts and chestnuts at the head of the bed. Kuniang and I were supposed to eat them, as a measure of sex-determination in our off-spring. Only thus would we be certain of having a son for ancestor worship. And one hundred days after Little Chink was born, the amah was found rubbing his mouth with the head of a chicken, the tail of a fish, and a crab. This would make it easier to teach him to eat!

The Five Virtues have lost their mother. *Lao tai-tai*, the Old Lady, is dead. She used to rule their household with a rod of iron. Kuniang and I disliked her intensely, but I think we both miss the little annoyances that she caused during so many years, before retiring into the gorgeous lacquer coffin that she kept stored (at my expense) in a temple on the southern side of the Tartar Wall.

Uncle Podger is still with us, but he is getting an old

dog. There are some white hairs on his muzzle, and he does not exert himself except when strictly necessary.

One evening, last winter, we were in my study after dinner. Kuniang was sitting on the floor in front of the fire, with a lot of typewritten manuscripts and a few copy-books spread out beside her. She had taken them from my old metal dispatch-box, which she had pulled out from its usual place near the bookcase.

I was at my desk, trying to follow Father Wieger's translation of the Annals of the first Han dynasty. The Chinese characters are printed on one side of the page and the French version on the other. But the chronicles are not easy to follow even with the use of a crib.

This is what I read:

'The Emperor Nai was a notorious sodomite. The documents concerning his relations with Tong-hien are the most numerous of the reign. The Emperor made over to Tong-hien the properties of two thousand families.'

I yawned and pushed back my chair. I did not really care what characters corresponded to those phrases. The glamour of a legendary Antinous did not attract me when I might watch the gold of Kuniang's hair, glinting in the firelight. So I went and sat on the sofa opposite Uncle Podger, who was sleeping on my best arm-chair. He had all that self-conscious repose of a dog that knows, even in its dreams, that it ought to be in its basket.

'What have you got there, Kuniang?' I asked.

'They are your stories; the ones you made me copy out, to give me something to do when you took me away from the Russian family.'

'Why spread them out on the floor?'

'It is the easiest way to see at a glance how many there are and what they are about.'

'Those copy-books are nothing of mine.'

'No. They are my old diaries.'

'What are you going to do with them all, now you have got them out?'

'I thought that perhaps you might make another volume, to continue The Maker of Heavenly Trousers.'

'Of my stories or of your diaries?'

'Don't be silly! My diaries tell the same tale that you wrote in the Heavenly Trousers, only from my point of view and with rather less restraint.'

'I remember you accused me of being too reticent.'

'Well, you see, you are hampered by having been brought up in the West. You don't mind what other people say, but you are particular about what you say yourself. You were careful, all through the book, never to mention your own name, although you made no mystery about mine. So like a man! I don't mind what I say. But then, I was brought up in the East.'

'I feel sure that an unexpurgated edition of your diary would make a best seller.'

Kuniang laughed. 'Publish it if you like,' she said. 'The background is the same as in your stories and the Heavenly Trousers.'

'That is so. It is the old, old Chinese background that has been the setting, throughout the ages, of so many stories.'

'Yes. And do you know? Sometimes when I read The Maker of Heavenly Trousers, I wonder if the background is not the only part that is true.'

'What do you mean?'

'Well, you see, I am in that story. And it is such a strange feeling, to read about myself and my surroundings and the people I live among. It is like seeing my reflection in a mirror. And I wonder which is the real Kuniang, the one who moves through those pages, or the one who reads.'

'You raise the doubt eternal, Kuniang. What is truth? What is fiction? Which is substance? Which is shadow? So many people have asked these questions: Pontius

Pilate and Pirandello, Socrates and Bernard Shaw. Those that read the *Heavenly Trousers* believe that Kuniang is there, in the book. But Uncle Podger, who does not read, knows that she is somewhere about the house. Or if she is out, she will turn up at meal-times, which is all that matters. Yet Uncle Podger himself may be the creation of an author's fancy. And so the doubt remains.'

Kuniang was silent for a little and then she said:

'Do you remember those Chinese pictures we bought at the Liu-li-chang, during the fair? Mountain scenery, with streams and camel-back bridges, and funny little old men in the dress of the Ming dynasty, walking along paths that disappear into the mist. If you gaze at those pictures long enough, especially if you're feeling sleepy, new details appear that you had not noticed at first. A little temple – shall we say? – high up near the sky, with the clouds for a doormat. I always think that Chinese stories, and your stories, are like those pictures.'

Kuniang talks of my 'stories.' But it would be more correct to call them sketches of a China that is passing away: ghosts of old Peking, when it was still the capital of a great country, stretching from northern steppes to tropical jungles, and from Tibetan highlands to the sea.

Not that things have changed much where we live. John Chinaman goes on earning his daily rice and eating it, begetting children and bringing them up, dying and indulging in gorgeous funerals, whoever happens to be ruling the country for him at the time. Here, as Kuniang says, is the old background, the drop-scene at the back of the stage, on which we come forward, each in turn, to say our little piece and pass away.

That is substance, even though we be shadows.

As it was Kuniang who made me publish this book, so it was Kuniang who chose the title. It requires some explanation.

The Shuang Liè Ssè, that is to say, the old temple which is now my home in Peking, is situated in the south-eastern corner of the Tartar City, in a position corresponding to that of the Forest of Pencils (the building where they used to hold the examinations for the Han Lin Academy) in the south-eastern corner. The main entrance looks out on to the Tartar Wall almost at its extreme end, west of the Shun Chih Men. My stables, which are situated beyond the garden, to the north, have a separate entrance, which is used by us as a back door. Strange to say, this gate also faces south (to make a gate facing south on the northern side of a dwelling requires some ingenuity). For the north is considered inauspicious.

To reach the stables from the Shuang Liè Ssè itself, one passes out of the garden through a door opening into a narrow passage-way between two walls. This passage emerges on to the stable yard, which is not contiguous with my garden, but is separated from it by a stretch of waste ground some seventy yards long and fifty broad. The building where the horses are housed is on the northern side of the stable yard (there is room for about thirty horses, though I only keep four), and the gate is to the south, opening out on to the waste plot of ground. My head stableman, by name *Tò-ching* or Pure Virtue, uses that plot as an exercise ground for the ponies. And the sparrows of the vicinity use it for dust baths in winter, and come and bathe there in the puddles after the summer rains. The gate, like all gates in China, is roofed with overhanging eaves of coloured tiles. Though it cannot compare with the main entrance, which is flanked by marble lions and giant acacias, it is far more imposing than any stable-door that I have ever seen in China or out of it. Perhaps this is because these stables were used by the soldiers of the Emperor's bodyguard. A picket of cavalry had their quarters here when one or other of the Manchu 'Banners' were on duty on the Wall.

The gate is called the Hsi Ch'iao Men, or Gate of the

Happy Sparrows. Hsi Ch'iao might also mean 'magpies'; you can have it both ways. But I prefer the usually accepted version.

It is not yet clear why I should give such a name to this book.

Kuniang and I argued about it for days.

She points out that it is through that minor gate that we pass, as a rule, when we go into the town. For though the waste plot of ground is surrounded on three sides by the walls of the Shuang Liè Ssè and of the stables, it communicates to the east with a narrow lane, or *hutung*, leading eastward in the direction of the Lake Palaces. This is a much more convenient road than that alongside the Wall. So it happens that, through the Gate of the Happy Sparrows, we go into the world outside our home. It leads, so to speak, into the side-issues of our lives. And whereas in *The Maker of Heavenly Trousers* I told about ourselves, in this book I tell of what lies beyond our threshold.

Also the title is of good augury (an important consideration in dealing with things Chinese). There is no great store of happiness in Peking, or in life itself. Let us be grateful if we can find a little of it among the humblest of God's creatures, just outside our own back door.

1 The Five Tigers

My chinese servants are known to a wide circle of
friends, acquaintances, and rivals as the Five Virtues.
And the Shuang Liè Ssè, where I live, is often called the
Home of the Five Virtues, which shows that everything
about the place is run more for their convenience than for
mine. Five is one of the mystic numbers, and the name
'Virtue' may well have been given ironically, on a prin-
ciple of *Lucus a non lucendo*.

It would be ungracious and ungrateful on my part, if I
did not add that the Five Virtues, on the whole, are good
servants. If their peculiarities often exasperate me, it is
also true that after many years we have got to know and to
understand each other's ways.

Yet when I heard of another family of Chinese servants
in Peking who were known to all and sundry as the Five
Tigers, I had a fellow-feeling for their employers, especially as the latter, being new to China and to Chinese
ways, were soon as helpless in the thrall of their domestic
staff as Agag in the hands of the Amalekites.

Lieutenant the Honourable Lionel Montresor arrived in
Peking to take up his duties at the British Legation Guard,
soon after his marriage to Dorothy Stokes, daughter of
the late Sir Ebenezer Stokes, who made a large fortune
out of boot-polish. The newly wedded couple, having
money to spare, decided not to avail themselves of the
rooms placed at their disposal in the Guard compound,
but to rent a house outside the Legation Quarter.

Dorothy Montresor had social ambitions. She wished to give dinners and dances, to receive the foreign ministers and their wives, and to become a leader of the 'smart set' in Peking. Her ideal was not difficult to realize. The cosmopolitan society of the Chinese capital was quite willing to be entertained by a hostess who was both pretty and rich. People appreciated the desire to give them a good time and tactfully ignored the connexion between the bride and the boot-polish.

The first step towards setting up house in Peking is the selection of a 'number-one boy'. The term boys, applied to domestic servants in the Far East, does not necessarily imply that they are young. In China a boy may be of any age. They are numbered according to their rank, and, like Government officials, form an imperium in imperio.

A house of any social standing in Peking boasts of a number one, a number two, and sometimes a number three boy, besides cook, chauffeur, gardener, etc., and numerous coolies. The latter, like scullions in feudal times, look after the fires, scrub the floors, wash the dishes, and perform the meaner domestic duties.

One of the most widely spread of general notions concerning China is that Chinese servants are superior to the servants of any other nationality. This legend, like many others, has a foundation in fact and a superstructure of fable. It describes the Chinese boy as one of the attractions of the Orient. It is an old joke to say that the Call of the East is 'Boy!'

A good number one boy – so one tells one friends at home – can procure anything from a table napkin to a palimpsest, and everything can be left to him, from the care of a canary to that of a lady friend. He is responsible for the peace and comfort of your home. He engages and dismisses the other servants, teaches them their duties, and is answerable for their good behaviour. The master of the house has nothing to think of; he need only express his wishes and complain if he is not well served.

This is all very fine, in theory. In practice the advantages of the system can only be realized if the boys are efficient. And good boys are as difficult to procure in China as good servants elsewhere.

The Five Tigers were brothers: servants of faultless training and perfect manners, but thieves one and all, without compunction and without limit.

One acted as first boy, another as second, another as third. One was stableman and another was cook. They worked together, but if a prospective householder desired to engage one or two of them separately, they would raise no objection. Sooner or later a reunion would be effected, either by persuading the new master that an increase in staff was desirable, or by procuring the expulsion of rival servants. The name which figures as title to this story was not conferred upon the brothers by a disillusioned employer, but by a fellow-servant who had been ousted to make room for one of the gang. And although the name itself was intended as a badge of infamy, the Five Tigers were proud of it. Beneath the family altar, where they burned incense to the shades of their ancestors, the eldest brother set out a little group of toys. Five tigers in stuffed leather stood in a row, their tails erect, their eyes starting fiercely out of their heads, and their sides marvellously striped in white and red and yellow.These toys represented, so to speak, the trade-mark of the firm.

The Five Tigers were taken on by the Montresors *en bloc* and given a free hand in the distribution of the household duties and of their own perquisites. It must be admitted that the Honourable Lionel and his wife were served as efficiently as they were robbed, which is saying a good deal. Their dinners could hardly have been surpassed in the best hotels in Paris, and they cost more.

Before entering the employment of the Honourable Lionel the Five Tigers had served and victimized a series of masters: a Major of Cavalry, noted for his epicurean tastes; a Commissioner of Customs who was a bit of a dandy; and a Minister-Plenipotentiary, who entertained largely and kept house as if he were ambassador in one of the greater capitals.

In the service of these employers, the Five Tigers had acquired considerable wealth, and had learnt to perform their duties to perfection. All five shared with other Orientals such characteristics as a quiet dignity of bearing, noiseless movements, and an unruffled calm. Moreover, they possessed a quality which is peculiar to the Chinese and enables them sometimes to become indeed those model servants, whose praises are sung by enthusiasts all the world over. This quality consists in the capacity of repeating any number of times, with unvaried success, any piece of work that they have once accomplished satisfactorily.

The advantages of being served by the Five Tigers were undeniable. Montresor's uniform was brushed and pressed and his boots were polished (with Stokes's patent blacking) as if by Beau Brummell's valet, which was all the more remarkable as those were still the days when the majority of foreigners in the Far East found it necessary to explain to their boys that shirt-studs should be put on with the clasps inside and that blacking is not meant for brown shoes or for patent leather.

I have already mentioned the excellence of the Montresor dinners. It has never been difficult to find a good cook in Peking since the far-off days when a certain French minister brought with him to China a chef by the name of Jules. Like certain master-craftsmen of the Renaissance, who left their native land to carry abroad the inspiration of their genius, Jules founded a school in the Orient and left a band of disciples to carry on the good work. One of Jules' *chefs-d'oeuvre* was a sweet known as Gâteau Saint Honoré, made of candied fruits and whipped cream. Long after the return of Jules and his master to Europe, the Gâteau Saint Honoré was served at the close of all banquets in Peking. It appeared occasionally at the dinners given by the Honourable Lionel and his bride, but by that time other foreign cooks had visited the Chinese capital and further developed its culinary possibilities.

The signal ability of the Five Tigers was also evident outside the normal routine of the house, and showed itself at its best in an emergency. Mrs. Montresor could invite twelve people to dinner, giving the cook barely an hour's notice and yet be sure that the guests would partake of the choicest food, cooked to perfection. She could arrange for picnics in far-away temples and in picturesque localities, difficult to reach, and long excursions to the Imperial tombs in mountain ranges to the east and to the west. Wherever she chose to go, her boys would provide excellent meals as a matter of course: cold dishes in summer and hot in winter. Nor was there anything picnicky about the bill of fare: *Mousse de volaille – Côtelettes de lièvre aux champignons – Pêches Melba*, followed by coffee and liqueurs, served neatly, quickly, and without noise or fuss.

Even the Five Tigers could not get rid of certain habits peculiar to their class. What they did in violation of the laws of hygiene in the kitchen and with the ice-chest, it is best not to inquire. And they would enter their employers' bedroom without knocking at any hour of the day or night. But out of respect for foreign idiosyncrasies, they would ascertain beforehand at the keyhole whether their mistress was in a costume and position to receive them, thus avoiding unpleasantness.

Now comes the reverse of the medal, as represented by the daily plunder, which trebled the expenditure of the Montresor household.

In addition to their pay, Chinese boys exact a commission on everything purchased by their master or for him. This they do whether he likes it or not, and their commission goes by the name of 'squeeze'. It is divided among the servants according to their rank. In China, the boys' squeeze, up to a certain point, is considered a legitimate perquisite. So was the percentage allowed to the court eunuchs, in the days of the empire, on the tribute that came in from the provinces. It is all a matter of proportion. If the number one boy is honest, he will not exact more than ten per cent. If he is not, the only limit lies in the employer's ability to defend himself, or in his capacity to pay.

The squeeze exacted by the Five Tigers started at a minimum of thirty per cent and often reached one hundred and even five hundred per cent *ad valorem* on the various articles brought into the house. But they had further sources of illicit gain, which formed the envy and admiration of other boys less fortunate in their opportunities.

They purchased, with a regularity that was much appreciated by the shopkeepers, three times the amount of provisions required for the house. The surplus was sold again for their own profit, slightly below cost price. The Five Tigers ended by setting up a shop of their own in the Tartar City, for the sale of provisions furnished by them out of the stock of the Montresor household. Boys from other houses were allowed to contribute, on payment of a commission, but the bulk of the merchandise came from the original investors, who held preference shares.

Some foreign storekeepers in the Legation Quarter showed nervousness at the underselling of their goods, but they were reassured when it was explained to them that those same goods had been originally imported by themselves. A second sale to Chinese customers or to the few foreigners who might scent a good bargain could only expedite the turnover to the profit of all concerned.

Like all Chinese houses, that which the Montresors had rented was made up of one-storied pavilions, each separate from the other. The new tenants had installed central heating at their own expense, so that it was possible to keep up a pleasant temperature throughout, even though one might have to cross the open courtyards in passing from one pavilion to another. The Five Tigers took advantage of this modern improvement and transformed the house into an inn. The pavilions set apart for the servants, the porter's lodge, the laundry, and the kitchen were nightly filled to overflowing by a crowd of Chinese, who paid from five to ten cents a head for the privilege of sleeping there. In winter-time the pavilion which contained the furnace for the steam-heating was the most sought after by the habitués of the 'Hôtel Montresor', and corresponded to the royal suite in fashionable hotels. It was reserved for clients who paid as much as twenty cents for a night's lodging. Chinese seem to prefer sleeping close together like sardines in a tin, so that at certain seasons the house harboured (all unbeknown to the hosts), over a hundred paying guests.

There was no lack of people who were willing and even eager to point out to Montresor and to his wife how they were being cheated. The Honourable Lionel's brother-officers and his wife's friends took care to warn them. The Colonel who commanded the British Guard spoke words of wisdom:

'Take my advice,' he said to Montresor, 'and every now and then give that number one boy of yours a good hiding. You may not know why you beat him. But, depend upon it, he will!'

Neither Montresor nor his wife paid much attention to these warnings. Before his marriage, the Honourable Lionel had found it difficult to make ends meet. The unaccustomed feeling of being able to spend money lavishly, even uselessly, was not unpleasant. His wife, on the other hand, knew that her own success as a hostess was largely due to the exceptional capabilities of her servants. She would never have been able to teach a new set of boys those intricate rules of domestic service that the Five Tigers knew to perfection.

So it happened that the brothers got off with an

occasional scolding, which they accepted in a proper spirit of contrition, promising to cut down expenses as much as possible. After which, things would go on as before, only more so.

One day in the Montresor household there occurred an incident not unusual among newly wedded couples. Husband and wife fell out. The cause of their disagreement is not known and has no bearing on this story. Bitter and apparently unforgivable things were said on both sides. Possibly the Honourable Lionel made some allusion to boot-polish, and she may have mentioned the bridegroom's debts, settled by her parents before the marriage. Whatever the cause, the offence was such that husband and wife were estranged, and they kept apart as much as possible. But they were careful not to wash their dirty linen in public, and when in company would take part in the general conversation, keeping up appearances as a model couple. In private they never spoke to each other.

The trouble arose in the early summer, when the social life of Peking passes through a period of comparative calm. There are no dances and few dinners. People who belong to the smart set, and those who do not, think only of sheltering from the almost tropical rains, and of mopping the moisture from their own perspiring brows.

It had been decided, some months before, that Mrs. Montresor should go to England during the summer, to visit her relations. Her place in the Trans-Siberian had been booked for the end of July. By tacit consent, the make-believe of conjugal felicity was kept on, pending her departure.

A few people guessed that something must have happened to destroy the harmony in the home. The Colonel's wife spoke to her husband on the subject. He confirmed her suspicions by mentioning that the Honourable Lionel had become an habitué of the Club and often took his meals there. The Colonel's wife was a sensible woman

22

and knew that, if the young bride did not confess her troubles, it was best not to interfere. So she confined herself to expressing a pious hope that things might right themselves before long. To which the Colonel replied by some vague remark on women in general, thus betraying the incompetence of a mere man in matters of so delicate a nature.

The hope expressed by the Colonel's wife might have been realized and the quarrel ended in 'blessings on the falling out that all the more endears', had it not been for the monthly bills.

On the first of each month, the Honourable Lionel found the household bills spread out on his writing-table. It was not possible for him, in the circumstances, to go to his wife for money, so he had to pay them himself. Before their quarrel, it had always been Mrs. Montresor who defrayed the common expenses. The fact that his wife had ceased to provide for the upkeep of the house proved how deep was her resentment. It also placed the Honourable Lionel in an extremely difficult position, as he possessed no income beyond his pay, which was totally inadequate to run a house on the lines laid down by the Five Tigers. Yet he could hardly refuse to pay the bills, without 'losing face' before the servants and his wife. Nor could he make overtures for a reconciliation, lest his motive be misunderstood. More than once he was on the point of seeking Mrs. Montresor in order to say something pleasant and conciliatory, when the sight of a pile of bills (unpaid) on his writing-table gave him pause.

One afternoon, shortly before the date fixed for his wife's departure, Montresor was sitting in the garden, when he heard shouts and the sound of people running. The next moment a coolie appeared with a pail, which he filled at a small pond, half-covered with lotus flowers, and then hurried off in the direction of the pavilion that served Mrs. Montresor as a boudoir. It was easy to guess what had happened: there had been a short circuit among the wires of the electric light. This often occurs during the summer months in Peking. The damp produced by the torrential rains is the cause of the trouble and also a safeguard against the fire spreading.

Montresor wished to ascertain the extent of the damage, and, knowing that his wife was out, he entered her boudoir. The wires had short-circuited while a coolie was polishing a standing lamp, with the light turned on. Little harm had been done: a few blackened wires and a smell of burning were the only signs of a mishap. Montresor was on the point of going out of the room when he noticed, on his wife's writing-table, a cheque-book and a pile of bills. The bills were written in Chinese characters, with an English translation on one side. Montresor picked one up and read:

BILL OF MA-FU

Give dinner three pony	36 dollars
Carrots	1 dollar
Chiffon	2 dollars
Puttee one shoe pony	80 cents
Pay ma-fu	20 dollars
TOTAL Dollars	59 and 80 cents

Underneath was written, in Mrs. Montresor's handwriting: '*Paid. July 10th.*'

It was a bill that Montresor himself had paid the day before. He remembered it perfectly. The inclusion of chiffon in a stable bill had struck him as odd. In answer to his inquiries, it had been explained by the head *ma-fu* that it meant cloths for polishing saddles and bridles.

Montresor examined the other bills that were lying on the table. Among them were several that he had paid himself. While absorbed in these investigations, he became aware that his wife had entered the room. She was watching him in obvious surprise and disapproval. But in the interest of his discovery, Montresor forgot for a moment how things stood between them, and, thinking only of the business in hand, he exclaimed:

'Oh! There you are. Just look at this . . .' He held out a sheaf of bills. 'Here is something that wants seeing to. Come into my study, will you?' With the bills in his hand, he strode off through the door that opened on to a veranda. Much astonished and slightly indignant, Mrs. Montresor followed him.

On reaching his study, Montresor looked over his own recent accounts. They fully justified his suspicions.

'How long,' he asked his wife, 'have you been paying the house bills?'

'I've always paid them,' she replied.

'All of them?'

'Yes. As far as I know.'

Montresor stared at her for a moment and then rang the bell. It was answered by the number one boy. His master addressed him sternly:

'I find,' he began, 'that for some time you have been presenting the same bills both to my wife and to myself. Both of us have paid them. This has been going on for at least two months. Will you kindly explain?'

If Montresor expected to note some sign of confusion in the face of his senior domestic servant, he was disappointed. The first of the Five Tigers was not easily put out of countenance. With the calm assurance of one whose conscience is untroubled, he replied:

'Master pay bills I give him. Missee pay bills my blother the cook give her. Perhaps makee mistake. Me no savvy.'

'Do you mean to tell me that you do not know what bills your brother the cook presents to us and how much money we give him?'

'No, master. I have quallel with my blother. We no speaky.'

Montresor looked his number-one boy in the face. The Chinese bore the scrutiny with a serene deference. No trace of a lurking smile on those impassive features. His expression was tranquil and austere. The Honourable Lionel felt beaten.

'You may go,' he said. 'We will speak of this later.'

When the boy had gone, Montresor looked at his wife and was surprised to see that she had buried her face in her handkerchief. For a moment he thought that she might be crying. A stifled gurgle betrayed the fact that she was trying not to laugh.

There was a silence.

Then Montresor asked:

'What do you say to a set of tennis?'

A few minutes later, they went out together, carrying their rackets. They were talking and laughing gaily.

From the windows of the surrounding pavilions, the Five Tigers watched them pass.

2   A Question of Etiquette

Mr. Tang is my Chinese teacher. A friend recommended him as being 'entirely without odour', a quality which has obvious advantages in a person with whom one has to work at the same table, in a closed room. Lord Redesdale was less fortunate. In his *Memoirs* he speaks of his Chinese teacher as being 'so transparently thin that he was almost able to see the garlic, which otherwise so richly asserted itself'.

Mr. Tang deserves the gratitude of many pupils who, like myself, take liberties with the Chinese language. His is not a patient nature, and I cause him acute mental anguish by my lack of subtlety in rendering the distinctions between the 'tones'. Also my indifference to appearances must be trying to one whose sensitiveness (and, I fear, whose poverty) makes life a continual struggle against 'losing face'.

Mr. Tang does not look more than twenty-five years old, but I believe he is nearing forty. He is always dressed in a black sleeveless jacket, worn over a long silken robe, but as a concession to foreign fashions he wears a Borsalino hat and carries a silver-handled umbrella (a gift from a former pupil).

Twice a week, on Mondays and Thursdays, Mr. Tang and I probe the mysteries of the Chinese language. During the first half-hour of our lesson, we go over the characters. Each character is printed on a separate piece of paper. Mr. Tang holds a number of these in his hand and places them one by one on the table before me.

27

Sometimes he sets down two or three in a row (that is to say, in a vertical line, one beneath the other), so as to form a sentence.

I am sometimes asked by foreigners: 'What is a Chinese character exactly?' But so far I have not hit upon an answer that satisfies them or me. To say that it is an ideogram is not quite correct, though the impression is pictorial. Professor Giles wrote that 'the student should accustom himself to look upon each character as a root idea, not as a definite part of speech.' This phrase may be clear to the expert. It means very little to a novice, who cannot understand how a dialogue (as reproduced in a novel) can be made up of root ideas and not of words.

When Mr. Tang gives me a character to read, there are two things I have to think of: the meaning and the phonetic equivalent. Nothing in the drawing itself offers a clue as to how to pronounce it, any more than the figures which represent the numbers, 1, 2, 3.

Mr. Tang places before me a character which represents a door, with a suffix which represents a mouth. A mouth at the door means 'to ask,' 'to beg', whereas an ear at the door means 'to hear', 'to listen'. In both cases the phonetic equivalent is Wén, but pronounced in different tones. I do not always remember the tones, and I say 'to listen', when I mean 'to ask.' This annoys Mr. Tang.

Kuniang speaks Chinese much better than I do, having learnt it as a child. But she never studied the characters or the philosophy underlying them. Yet these give charm and fascination to the written language. That one woman under a roof should represent 'peace'; two women under a roof 'discord'; and three women under a roof 'gossip', offers conclusive evidence of an ancient wisdom.

Even when one knows the meaning and the modulations of the voice that correspond to each character, the difficulties are not all overcome. One has to discover what each one signifies within the sentence. I remember once Mr. Tang placed four characters in line. I read them aloud: 'Shuè-Yu-Ta-Yuan.' These monosyllables mean 'Water-centre-large-rotundity.' I made a courageous attempt at a translation: 'In the middle of round water (a hip bath?) is a large person.' I was wrong. It was a poetical allusion to the moon setting in the sea.

After wrestling with the characters, Mr. Tang and I indulge in conversation. When I have written a story with a Chinese setting, I read it aloud to Mr. Tang, partly to hear his opinion, and partly to provide a subject for our talk. As I read, Mr. Tang criticizes, and his comments are often more interesting than my story. His innate courtesy makes him reluctant to find fault, and as a rule he only points out the mistakes that I make in the interpretation of the Rites, those ceremonial observances so dear to the heart of every Chinaman of the old school. In matters concerning the Rites, Mr. Tang is inflexible. A story of mine, entitled *Old China*, met with his out-spoken disapproval.

The hero of my story was a Chinese minister, rich in honours and wives and concubines. His name was Hsiang. The story told how Hsiang decided to commit suicide *more sinico*, as a protest against the reforming policy of the Emperor Kuang-hsu. He arranged to take his own life at the date fixed for his next audience with the Emperor. According to an ancient custom, these audiences took place at night, some hours before the dawn. As the gates of the Tartar City used to be closed at sunset, any one who lived in the Chinese city and wished to pass at night to the inner side of the Tartar wall had to betake himself at the stroke of midnight to the principal southern gate, the Ch'ien Men. For only at midnight did the city gate open for a few minutes, to admit those who had business in the Winter Palace.

For the last time, Hsiang prepared a Memorial to the Throne, setting forth his opinions. It was written in his own hand, in tiny thread-like characters, such as were prescribed for reports to the Son of Heaven. The beautiful minute calligraphy was in itself a proof of the high degree of culture attained by the author. On the night of the audience, Hsiang enclosed the memorial in a lacquer box and dressed himself in robes of state, with a sable coat and an official hat, surmounted by a coral button. A short plume of peacock's feathers was attached to the brim of his hat and fell on the right shoulder. Before leaving the house, he spoke with his number one wife and gently caressed his sleeping children. Then, escorted by servants bearing lanterns, he made his way through the courtyards to where his private cart was waiting, drawn by a handsome grey mule. Thus he set out on his last journey.

Peking carts have a hood made of felt and resembling the *felze* of a Venetian gondola. The driver sits on the shaft. There are no seats, and you recline on the floor of the cart and can look through the black veil windows. No one can see within. By lowering the front curtain, you can be invisible even to the driver.

On the way from his house to the imperial palace, Hsiang committed suicide. He had brought with him a leaf of gold, rather like the silver paper they put round chocolates. In the darkness of the Peking cart, he inhaled this leaf, closing the respiratory passages and producing suffocation. The driver, all unsuspecting, urged on the grey mule and hurried through the empty streets. Death by means of a gold leaf is an aristocratic form of suicide, known in China as 'eating gold'.

In my story, I had let myself go over the description of the silent drive to the palace. I lingered over the scene at the Ch'ien Men, where the cart halted, while the guards opened the massive gates, studded with bronze knobs which caught the torchlight. Then I described the arrival of Hsiang's cart at the Forbidden City; the salute of the Manchu Bannermen as it passed under the gloomy arches, the hurried approach of eunuchs to help the

30

minister descend; their respectful pause to await his pleasure; the dawning surprise and doubt when no sign came; the breathless horror when the truth was known. Hurried footfalls in silent courtyards. A timid approach of news-bearers to the Pavilion of Mind Nurture, where the Son of Heaven gave audience. The announcement, made in fear and trembling, to the Emperor who sat on high, half veiled in shadow. A vague hope that the minister's death might have been a natural one; a hope dispelled by the first words of his memorial, witness of a brave man's despair.

At this point, Mr. Tang, who had been fidgeting in his chair as if he could bear it no longer, burst out with:

'But the Rites? You ignore the Rites!'

'What Rites?' I asked.

Mr. Tang stared at me more in pain than in anger. Then he added:

'The Rites prescribed for suicide. What you describe would not enter the head of any respectable person.'

'Why not?'

'It is contrary to the most elementary rules of etiquette.'

'In what way?'

'In every way. A man of the world, a Secretary of State, does not kill himself in an underhand manner, without bidding farewell to his family and giving instructions for the future. And it would be inadmissible to commit suicide within the walls of Peking.'

'Why not in Peking?'

'Because it is the Imperial City. Surely you know that! When you write the two characters Ch'in Ch'ang, you give them double elevation, beginning a new line. To seek death within the Tartar City would be a crime of *lèse-majesté*. Only an empress might do such a thing, as Lung Yu is said to have done, or some Imperial concubine, who might not leave the palace. But a minister, never! His protest would lose all weight as a final argument. One should kill oneself in the open country, as

Wu-ko-tu did, when he wished to protest because in choosing the heir to the throne the dynastic laws had not been respected. He hanged himself on a tree, in the region of the tombs. That was the right thing to do. Why don't you write the story of Wu-ko-tu?'

'It has been told before. Do you not know of any other and less important case of suicide in Chinese history?'

Mr. Tang sipped a cup of tea as he thought the matter over. At last he said:

'There must have been many other cases, but at present I can only remember one, and it happened very long ago.'

'All the better. My story is called *Old China*. Who was the suicide?'

'He was a philosopher and a member of the Han Lin Academy, who from time to time went to pay a visit to a prince. Each time they prepared for him a dish of turnips with salt. But one day he paid his visit, and though he waited a long time, no turnips were served. So he committed suicide.'

'He did what?'

'He committed suicide. Not at once, of course, but a few days later, at the foot of the Western Hills, in conformity with the Rites.'

'Merely because he did not have turnips with salt?'

'Yes. That dish, served to him during every visit, had become a Rite of courtesy. Not to have offered it was equivalent to a humiliation. Rather than accept the affront, he killed himself.'

'But, my dear Mr. Tang, if I were to write a story about an educated man, a scholar and a philosopher, who committed suicide because, when calling on a prince, he was not offered a dish of turnips with salt, nobody in my country would believe it. They would say it was all nonsense.'

'And if you write a story about a Chinese minister who commits suicide in a cart, within the walls of Peking, while on his way to the palace, anybody who knows China would say it was impossible, and that you are ignorant of our manners and customs.'

'Would that matter very much?'

'Of course it would! And I would lose face, who do my poor best to teach you.'

Far be it from me to make my old friend, Mr. Tang, lose face. So I have torn up the manuscript of *Old China*. But I am sorry, for it was a good story.

3   Under the Buddha's Eyes

Among the foreign missionaries in China, there are many to whom I owe a debt of gratitude for kind hospitality offered me in near and distant provinces. Two of these ecclesiastics (both Italians) were known to me even before I settled in Peking. They are men of very different stamp, though representative, each in his own way, of that band of Catholic pioneers who, in a changing world, carry on the work that Matteo Ricci began four centuries ago.

We first made friends on board ship, during a journey from Genoa to Shanghai, when I was still new to China (it was my first voyage to the Far East). So it happened that my initial knowledge of the country and its ways was obtained from these two ecclesiastics. And ever since my outlook on things Chinese has been tinged with their charitable scepticism.

Of my two friends, one is Monsignor Paoli, a bishop at thirty-six, whose diocese is almost as large as Italy, though lost in the wilds of Mongolia. He is of the type of missionary saints, modest, gay, and unaffected, who inspire sympathy even among the most anti-clerical, as well as a sense of regret that such men should pass their lives far from the busy world, which has need of such as they.

He is a fine-looking man, with clear-cut features and a glance both penetrating and serene. A long beard lends dignity to his appearance, without appreciably adding to his age. A certain air of youthfulness is one of his chief characteristics, a youthfulness of temperament that defies the passing years. To hear him talk, you would think that life in his diocese were a joyous thing and that the wind-swept grasslands beyond the Gobi desert were no less pleasant than the vine-clad slopes above Lake Como, where he was born.

My other friend, Padre Ignazio, is a Jesuit, attached to the Zi-ca-wei observatory. I doubt if he will remain long in China, though as a recognized authority on Oriental matters, he has been given leave to reside here, pending the completion of certain studies, of which a history of China, from the beginning of missionary endeavour there, is to be the result. He is of medium stature and of sturdy build. A sedentary life threatens his waistline. His features are Napoleonic; the nose is small and slightly aquiline, the mouth thin-lipped and resolute. His eyes are jet-black and, though full of expression, reveal nothing of what passes in his mind.

Whereas Monsignor Paoli gives one the impression of a man who has lived in the open and struggled against the elementary forces of nature, Father Ignazio has the white hands and the suave manner of the typical Vatican prelate. They were at school together, these two, and students at the same seminary. When they meet, they lapse once more into the old schoolboy language and talk of serious subjects with a gay light-heartedness, so that one seems to catch the other's smile. The mere fact of being together causes them to brim over with high spirits. They chaff one another, and quarrel and indulge in fits of merriment over the silliest jokes, or over no joke at all. For this reason they like to meet informally in my house, unfettered by the company of their colleagues and subordinates. Yet under their light-heartedness and under their gaiety, one feels the firmness of purpose, the foresight that thinks in centuries, the deep reserve of men whose aims reach far beyond their own fleeting lives. This attitude, though hardly perceptible in their daily work, yet creates a point of contact and serves to bring them into closer touch with the Chinese, to whom time means less than it does to us.

'You have chosen your diocese well!' Father Ignazio remarked to his friend, one day last April, after lunch on my veranda. 'If what I hear of Mongolia is true, there is one inhabitant every hundred square miles. You baptize four people and write to Rome that you have converted a province. Thus you pave the way for your beatification!'

'It seems to me,' replied Monsignore, carrying the war into the enemy's country, 'that you have not done badly yourself, with your precious history. You expand Father Wieger's translation of the Annals and quote a few English and French historical works. Meanwhile you pass three or four years in China, which might have been spent no less profitably in the library of the Propaganda Fide in Rome.'

'Would you believe it' Father Ignazio exclaimed, turning to me. 'This morning I went with him to buy provisions for the winter, and he ordered two barrels of brandy (and good brandy, too!) and two hundred packets of cigars. And then he talks of hardships. Lucky for him that he is constitutionally thin. If I gave myself up to such monastic good living, I would acquire the girth of Falstaff.'

'Monastic good living, indeed!' protested Monsignore. 'Forty degrees centigrade below zero and the wind off the frozen marshes ... If we did not keep sufficient alcohol in the house, by the end of the year there would be few of us left.'

'What about the cigars?'

'A luxury, I admit. But when one lives at a thousand miles from civilization, some little luxury is necessary, to chase away the blues.'

'Is it true,' I asked, with the laudable intention of changing the subject, 'that a Chinese traveller arrived at your mission during the winter in an open cart, with his legs frozen, so that they had to be amputated?'

'Quite true. When we asked him why he had not

thought of walking to warm himself, he replied that he had paid to travel by cart.'

The last time Monsignor Paoli came to Peking, we went for an excursion, he and I and Father Ignazio, to the Summer Palace. Father Ignazio was in great form. He had been reading *l'Ile des Pengouins*, and he said that Monsignore reminded him of the short-sighted saint, who arrives in a boat at an island in the Arctic seas, and mistaking the penguins on the shore for human beings, baptizes them on the spot.

Monsignore turned to me. 'What did I tell you?' he said. 'This is an example of the studies he is pursuing in China!'

Much to our surprise, when we reached the gates of the Summer Palace, a young Chinese, dressed in foreign clothes, came up and held out his visiting card. On it was engraved the legend: *Monsieur Jean Jacques Wu*.

In those days a permit was required to visit the Summer Palace. On receiving our request for this document, the Chinese authorities had taken note of the fact that one of our party was a bishop, and they had thought it incumbent on themselves to furnish him with a personal guide. It was in this capacity that Mr. Wu now presented himself. At first his company put a damper on our good humour. But we cheered up when we discovered that, although most kind and obliging, Mr. Wu was hardly qualified to act as a guide to the Summer Palace, never having been there before. He spoke French, and his contribution to our knowledge consisted in repeating before every work of art or picturesque landscape:

'*C'est très apprécié ici!*'

During the morning we visited the houses, temples, and terraces of what is known as the New Summer Palace, and the theatre where the Dowager Empress used to act, taking the part of the Goddess of Mercy, with the chief eunuch, Li Lien-ying, in the principal role.

Mr. Wu was wearing patent leather boots, which may have been rather tight. Towards eleven o'clock he began to show signs of fatigue, and his inevitable expression of praise, *C'est très apprécié ici!* sounded less convincing. When he heard that we intended to prolong our excursion, visiting the Jade Fountain and the Old Summer Palace, he begged to be excused, saying that he had an appointment in town. We parted with expressions of regret and feelings of mild satisfaction.

The Old Summer Palace interested Father Ignazio because he intended to describe its vicissitudes in his history. Monsignore and I were quite pleased to follow him about, and after long and sometimes arduous peregrinations, he led us into the grounds surrounding the Jade Fountain. This is a spring, forming a little lake, with cold green lights that remind one of the colours of jade.

As a historian, Father Ignazio's interest in this pleasance centred round the burning of the Summer Palace, by order of Lord Elgin, in 1860. The damage done on that occasion, and the subsequent neglect, have not diminished the charm of the abandoned palace. Some of its ruins are no less impressive than the more recent palace, built by the Dowager Empress. Three pagodas (one of which is of majolica) rise tall and straight, like cypresses round Fiesole. Temples with sandal-wood columns are mirrored in the jade-coloured waters; marble colossi keep watch under scented pines, and the hum of bees round calm-faced Buddhas renews the forgotten homage of droning prayer. But the millet stalks grow tall in the dried-up beds of lotus pools, and globe-trotters wander beneath the pleasure dome that an imperial will decreed. Chinese peasants, men and women, indistinguishable in their faded blue rags, rake the dusty soil to garner in a few dried grasses on the hillside where once the Son of Heaven rested from the splendours of the Dragon Throne.

We consumed various bottles of lemonade in a little

aerated water factory which now occupies a pavilion near the boathouse. One of the Emperor's barges was still afloat, and another had sunk to the bottom, with a rotting hull. We admired its graceful lines while we ate some sandwiches that we had brought from Peking. The energy that had inspired us in the morning, and had deprived us of the company of Mr. Wu, gave place after lunch to a preference for sedentary contemplations. Nevertheless we climbed laboriously to a pavilion which stands in a gap between two hills. It appeared to be of more recent construction than the other buildings, but it was no less empty and desolate. We came upon a caretaker in the outer courtyard, an old man, who on catching sight of me began to bow and smile with enthusiastic reverence. At first I was unable to explain such cordiality, but I recognized him when he asked for news of his grandson. The latter, a rather stupid boy of seventeen, afflicted with a painful stammer, is employed in my household in the capacity of *tingchai*, or letter-carrier. The old man, once a Manchu Bannerman, belonged to the Imperial Guard of Archers. He claims acquaintance with me since the days of the Boxer troubles, and even pretends that he saved my life, though I have no recollection of such an episode. I cannot even imagine how it could have happened, unless he means that he once had a shot at me and missed.

Whatever our relationship had been in the past, the meeting in the Summer Palace was fortunate, for the old bannerman, who in more prosaic times had become a caretaker, showed us exactly what we wanted: a pleasant spot to rest in. He bustled about in eager hospitality, carrying up a small table and three rickety but not uncomfortable wicker chairs. Then, still asking after Kuniang and the Five Virtues and Little Lu, he made us some tea and served it in old green-grey cups. The spot that he took us to, and where we rested, was a gallery, some sixty feet long, overlooking the Old Summer Palace and a corner of the New. It had been open to the air, but some recent occupier had closed it with glass. The place may once have been occupied by foreigners, for in the years just after 1900 some of these buildings were taken over as country residences by members of the foreign legations. Many of the glass panes were broken, but enough remained to afford protection from the wind, which was beginning to blow off the hills.

Our conversation as we sat there, drinking the tea which the archer had brought us, turned naturally to the destruction of the Summer Palace and to the events that led up to it. We all knew how Lord Elgin's decision had been provoked. During a halt in the advance of the Anglo-French forces from Tientsin, a party of foreign officers and interpreters had proceeded to the Chinese camp, according to a prearranged plan, to conclude an armistice. They had been traitorously captured and hurried off to the Summer Palace, where the Emperor Hsieng Feng was in residence with his court. There they had been subjected to such ill-treatment that many of them died.

Monsignor Paoli admitted that reprisals were necessary, but he deplored the vandalism which had destroyed many of the finest treasures of Chinese art.

'Lord Elgin,' answered Father Ignazio, 'has been blamed by many historians, but his critics do not suggest what else he could have done. Only by striking at the Emperor through his possessions, was it possible to punish him and not other people who were not responsible for the outrage. If Lord Elgin had said to the Chinese representatives: "You must cut off the heads of those who captured and tortured our envoys," they would have complied with his demand. It is easy and even convenient to empty the prisons with executions en masse. One hundred or one thousand heads would have been forwarded to the allied camp. And all those people would have gone to their death without knowing why; at most they would have been told that it was to placate the foreign devils. An exemplary punishment would have ended in a parody of justice, and the Emperor would have laughed in his sleeve at the foreigner's simplicity.'

Monsignor Paoli shook his head. 'I am not questioning the political wisdom of such a punishment,' he said. 'But I mourn the departed glories. This palace embodies the artistic genius of China. It is beautiful still, despite the fire and half a century of neglect. Think what it must have been before 1860!'

'True,' said Father Ignazio. 'But whose the fault of the destruction? You must not attribute it all to Lord Elgin. The flames, kindled at his order, did relatively little damage; certainly less than the long spoliation, continuing even to this day. The gardens in Peking, and not a few in Europe and America are full of marbles and majolicas, taken from these ruins. As with the Colosseum, *Quod non fecerunt barbari fecerunt Barberini*. The looting was started by the Chinese themselves. In the absence of any guardians to the palace, the Son of Heaven was despoiled by his own subjects. For such marauders, the proximity of foreign troops was not a deterrent; it offered unheard-of opportunity. The French soldiers noticed that smoke was rising from one of the pavilions. A Chinese mob had penetrated into the Palace, scaling the walls with ladders. They were now laying hands upon the treasure. From that moment, Bedlam broke loose and the looting became general. The foreign soldiers thought, naturally enough, that if the valuables were to be stolen anyhow, it might as well be done by those who had a wrong to avenge. The commanders attempted to keep order, but with scant success.'

'If this is true, where does Lord Elgin come in?' I asked.

'He was not originally responsible for the looting. It was afterwards, when he heard what had been done to the men who were carried off before the battle of Pa-li-kao, that he decided to complete the work so well begun and set fire to the pavilions. The smoke, carried eastward by a languid breeze, hung over Peking, like a symbol of wrath.'

41

Monsignor Paoli had a bright idea. 'Your friend, the archer,' he said to me, 'must remember the destruction of the Summer Palace. Ask him to tell us about it.'

The old archer was standing by, ready to fill our tea-cups when required. On being questioned, he said that he remembered the arrival of the foreigners and how they set fire to the palace. His 'Banner' was then guarding the north-west corner of the Tartar City. Father Ignazio asked:

'And did you understand for what reason the *In-guo Chin-chai* (British minister) burnt those pavilions?'

'Yes. I understood.'

'Why was it done?'

'So that no one might know how much he had stolen.'

We gazed at the old man open-mouthed. Father Ignazio laughed.

'These people,' he said, 'always accept the version that is favourable to themselves and discreditable to the foreigner. It would be only fair to add that such an attitude is not limited to the Chinese.'

We were all silent for a few moments, and then Monsignore asked: 'Did any one ever know the fate of the captives who were brought here in 1860?'

Father Ignazio replied: 'Only of those who escaped with their lives, and of others who had died before their eyes. The survivors could not tell what had happened to some of their comrades, who were never seen or heard of again. The prisoners that were brought here were tied hand and foot with ropes, and water was thrown on the ropes to tighten them. They were left for days, lying on the stone flags of the courtyards. Many died of the festering wounds produced by ropes that cut into their flesh. Theirs was a cruel death, even though there was no highly imaginative torture, such as the Red Indians used to inflict on the first missionaries in North America. When a Chinese wishes to be cruel, he shows it more by his indifference to a prolonged suffering than by any refinement of *Schadenfreude*.'

'Refinement of what?'

'*Schadenfreude*. It is a German word and means "pleasure in suffering": presumably the suffering of others. You might call it a primitive form of humour. In the feudal castles of Germany and Austria, one can still see instruments of torture that are miracles of ingenuity. Here in China, the old punishment of the *kang* could hardly be called torture, though the heavy wooden collar that prevented the hands from reaching the head, must have produced acute discomfort, amounting to pain. On the other hand, it is still quite common to see prisoners slowly dying of hunger and of hardships to which their warders are utterly indifferent. Lord Elgin himself freed the Chinese prisoners whom he found in jail, simply because their condition filled him with horror.'

'I wish I could do the same in Mongolia,' said Monsignor Paoli. 'I was unable to sleep for many nights, thinking of what I had seen in a local prison. There was a large room, full of closed wooden boxes. They were shaped like coffins, but higher and not so long. On one side there was a hole, just large enough for a hand to pass through. Inside each box was a prisoner. Once a day a warder came into the room and gave food and drink to any one who put out his hand to receive it.'

'And how long were those unfortunates kept there?'

'They never came out. Once a box was closed, with some one inside, it was never opened again. If for three or four consecutive days no supplicatory hand appeared at meal-time, the box and its contents were buried.'

I shuddered, and not wishing to think of the dreadful boxes, turned once more to the old archer. He had told us that he had been on duty at the north-eastern corner of the Tartar City, so it was without much hope of his being able to give us first-hand information that I asked him if he remembered the foreign prisoners who were brought to the Summer Palace before the Emperor fled to Jehol. To my surprise, he answered Yes. (Possibly what he had said before was not true).

Father Ignazio, hoping to hear some particulars that might be of historical interest, asked the old man to relate what had happened. But the archer did not respond readily to questions of a general character. A patient examination was necessary to extract from him anything in the shape of a narrative. So we began by asking how old he had been at the time. He could not tell off-hand, but he said that he had been born in the twenty-second year of the reign of Tao Kwan. From this we calculated that in 1860 he must have been seventeen years old.

'How many prisoners did you see?' asked Father Ignazio.

'I saw two. But there were others that I did not see.'

'And what did they do to those two?'

'Nothing was done to them. They lay on the ground, tightly bound.'

'And no one troubled about them?'

'There were some boys in the courtyard. They tormented the prisoners and dropped dung on them.'

'C'est très apprécié ici,' I murmured, in imitation of Mr. Wu.

'And what happened in the end to those two prisoners?'

'One died. The other succeeded in escaping, but afterwards he died too.'

'Why should they die, if no one did them any harm?'

'One was old.'

'I see. He died of old age. And the one who escaped, where did he go to?'

'He hid in the grotto of the Buddhas, not far from here.'

'Did they catch him again?'

'No. They did not catch him.'

Father Ignazio paused in his questioning and said to us: 'There might be something of interest in this episode, but the old man is not very communicative.'

Monsignor Paoli took a turn at asking questions:

'How was it that he succeeded in escaping if he was bound?'

'I helped to loosen the ropes.'

'You did! And why?'

'He promised me some gold pieces that he had hidden in his belt.'

'You did not think of taking them while he was still bound?'

'No. He might have called the sentinels, and then they would have taken the money themselves.'

'You are a prudent man. And do you happen to know what the prisoner was called?'

'I do not know. But he wrote his name in the grotto of the Buddhas. It may be possible to read the characters.'

'That is a good idea,' exclaimed Father Ignazio. 'Let us go and see this grotto.'

In the Old Summer Palace, there are two grottoes, whose walls are adorned with effigies of the Buddha in relief. The larger one, at the foot of a hill, is easy of access. The other is near the summit, and the entrance is so well hidden that few people know of its existence. It was to this cave that the archer led us after a stiff climb up the hill-side. An almost invisible opening on the grassy slope could only be reached by climbing over some rocks, and one could pass out again higher up. The sides of the grotto were of granite, a grey granite with hardly any trace of mica. But here and there the stone disappeared under a surface of hardened earth, which might have been the result of a gradual deposit, during centuries, of minute particles of dust borne by the wind.

The Buddhas were carved in the rock, and many of them were real works of art. Their expression was austere and they wore classical Oriental draperies. Other carvings represented evil spirits which trampled human beings under foot and wore necklaces of severed heads. Forgetting for a moment what we had come for I stopped and stared up at the finest of these images. It was a Buddha, isolated from his fellows on an otherwise unsculptured space of wall, and far superior to them for the beauty of his features. He seemed to impersonate the aloofness that is characteristic of Oriental divinities, for whom salvation lies in withdrawal. The Buddha looked down through half-closed eyes, serene, but without hope.

The old archer pointed out the wall on which the fugitive had carved his name. But here we met with a disappointment: other visitors to the grotto had done likewise. At least fifteen names disfigured the surface of the rock. Monsignore turned to our guide and asked:

'Do you remember more or less where the first name was written?'

The old man pointed out an inscription in rough letters all out of the straight. Some of the letters appeared to have been obliterated, possibly because the surface of the wall, though smooth, was of varied consistency, the hard stone alternating with the more fragile accumulation. The inscription ran thus:

RATE

RO AN MA

ELMI

E

X 1860

We gazed at those letters in silence. For my part I was doubtful if the inscription could be the one we sought. I was surprised when Father Ignazio said confidently:

'Our friend has brought us to the right spot. But what a pity that the surname is illegible. However, we know that the second or the third letter was an E.'

'What does it mean?' I asked.

'Do you not see? The first letters of each word are missing. Perhaps because the writer traced those letters on the granite, close to the deposit of earth, and the upper stratum is no longer the same. In the date the day of the month is also missing, but that may be because the poor man did not remember how many days had passed since he had been taken prisoner. If I guess rightly, the inscription should read:

> 'ORATE
> PRO ANIMA
> WILHELMI
> ... E
> X 1860'

'In Latin!' I exclaimed.

'Yes, in Latin. Which shows that he was an educated man. And he must have felt his end approaching, otherwise, why ask for a prayer for his soul?'

The old archer watched us, well pleased at our interest. Father Ignazio continued to examine the inscription. He took a penknife from his pocket and began to scrape the wall a little above the word ORATE. Then he did the same a little farther down, to the right.

'Take care,' I said. 'You will break the point of the blade.'

He stopped scraping and said: 'I only wanted to try the consistency of the surface. It is difficult to understand why any one, having so much space on which to carve his name, should choose just this spot where the hard stone gives place to the softer earth. But I realize that, on account of the thick stratum of dust over all, it feels the same to the touch.'

'That may be,' said Monsignore. 'But the different substances are clearly visible, unless for some reason one should work in the dark.'

Father Ignazio seemed absorbed in his own thoughts. Then he turned to the old archer with the sudden question:

'Was it you who blinded him?'

At the unexpected accusation, the old archer stepped back as if from a blow:

'No, Great Master! It was not I. The boys in the courtyard did it. I helped him. I cut his bonds while the

47

sentries slept. I led him up here. I brought him rice and water. . . .'

'And he died in this cave?'

'No. He went forth alone, instead of waiting for me to guide him. He fell among the rocks.'

'Why should he want to go out?'

'The foreign devils had arrived. They were close under the hill. He wished to join them.'

'How could he guess they were so near?'

'He heard the drums and the trumpets.'

'Did he die immediately, when he fell among the rocks?'

'No. Not immediately. After two days.'

'Why did you not call his own people to help him?'

'I dared not. I was afraid. I fled into the city.'

'What were you afraid of?'

'They might have thought it was I who hurt him.'

Father Ignazio ceased his questioning and began to copy out the inscription in his note-book. How had he guessed that the writer had been blind? Perhaps from the uncertainly traced letters and the choice of an unsuitable surface.

While we stood there, I tried – and I think the others were doing likewise – to reconstruct the tragedy that had occurred in that same grotto, more than half a century before: the sufferings of the escaped prisoner, blind and alone among the carven Buddhas; the words so painfully scratched on the wall as he felt death approaching. Then suddenly in his bitter darkness, the roll of drums and the notes of a bugle in the plain. At that sound, which promised help and safety, the uncertain steps on the hill-side, the sudden fall, the prolonged agony, while the Chinese soldier spied on him from afar.

'No need to ask anything more,' said Father Ignazio. 'When we get home I will make inquiries. It may not be impossible to ascertain who the man was.'

He turned to leave, but Monsignor Paoli made a sign to stop us.

'We can still do for him,' he said, 'that which he asked.'

Father Ignazio looked puzzled. 'Do what?'

'Say a prayer for his soul.'

And, kneeling in the dust, under the eyes of the smiling Buddhas, he began to recite a prayer from the Mass for the dead:

> 'Requiem aeternam dona eis, Domine,
> Et lux perpetua luceat eis . . .'

At the sound of that declaiming voice, a bat emerged from the shadows above us and fluttered out into the open air. The old archer stood at the entrance to the cave, his bent figure silhouetted against the evening sky. Father Ignazio, his face bent in the palm of his hand, intoned the responses.

Outside, on the slope of the hill, the birds were calling one another to rest.

4   Transfiguration

'And he was transfigured before them. . . .'

ST. MATT. xvii. 2

There are two characters in this story. Let me introduce them separately.

One was a Chinese boy, sixteen years old, who tended his father's goats to the south of the Chinese city. His name was Ur-ko, which means 'two dogs' (ur – two; ko – dog). It had been given to him in consequence of a complicated vow, made by his parents before his birth, to the god who brings children (one of the divinities that are worshipped in the big temple just outside the Ch'ao Yang Men). He was to be given that name on condition that he was a boy.

I made the acquaintance of Ur-ko one day when riding along the open space between the southern wall of the Chinese City and the wall that encloses the Temple of Heaven. These two walls run parallel for about a mile, and the ground between them is well suited for a canter; it is hardly ever used, except by foreigners who wish to exercise their ponies. My saddle girths having suddenly come loose, I dismounted and discovered that a strap was broken. Fortunately the *ma-fu*, Pure Virtue, who was riding behind me, had a piece of string in his pocket. What the Chinese can do with a piece of string must be seen to be believed. They will mend a motor-car with one, let alone a saddle-strap. He at once set to work to put things right for me, showing all the characteristic ability of his race in makeshifts of every kind.

We were standing half-way down the corridor between the two walls, with no one in sight in either direction, when suddenly both our ponies shied violently. For a few moments Pure Virtue and I had our work cut out to prevent them pulling the reins out of our hands and bolting. When we succeeded in quieting the ponies, we looked round to see what had caused their alarm. A boy with a large conical hat, like those you see in Japanese ivories, had emerged from among the grasses alongside the wall of the Temple of Heaven; he had risen apparently straight out of the earth, and for a moment I thought that he must have been lying there asleep. But an indignant question from Pure Virtue, whose arm had almost been pulled out of its socket, elicited the information that the boy had come out from the Temple of Heaven through a drain under the wall.

Puzzled by this explanation, I went and examined the ground, giving my pony to the boy himself to hold. Thus I discovered that, every two hundred yards or so, there was an aperture in the foundations of the temple wall, to allow the waters to pass out when the low-lying land within the park became flooded with the summer rains. These apertures had a double row of bars; thick bars of stone, to support the wall above, and behind them a row of iron bars, set so close together that nobody could possibly squeeze through. But the iron bars were old and rusty, and a brief examination revealed the fact that some of them were loose in their sockets and with a little trouble might be taken out and put back again. With one bar missing, a slim boy might well slip into the sacred precincts. This is what our young friend had been up to, instead of tending his father's goats, which were grazing in the corridor between the walls.

When I returned from inspecting the drain, I found Pure Virtue and the boy deep in conversation. I stood by and listened to what they were saying, and it was thus that I learned that the boy's name was Ur-ko; also that,

51

six months before, he had had a terrible illness, since when his parents had obliged him to wear ear-rings, in the hopes that the evil spirits might take him for a little girl and not trouble him (little girls are hardly worthy of any self-respecting spirit's attention).

The conical hat and the ear-rings were almost all that Ur-ko had on. The rest of his costume consisted in a triangular slip of red cotton, attached to a string round his waist. Practically naked as he was, I could not help admiring the exceptional beauty of the boy's figure. He was tall and splendidly modelled, with a slender waist and fine broad shoulders. Seldom have I seen such statuesque lines as in this poor goatherd. His face also was handsome, with a rather wistful expression. Like most Chinese, he had fine hands and feet.

When Pure Virtue had mended the strap, we mounted our ponies once more, and I gave the boy some coppers, which he held in his hand, having nowhere else to keep them.

So much for my first personage. Now for the second. She was no less (I quote from her visiting card) than 'Miss Amelia Peterkin Wallace of Lake Side Drive, Chicago, Ill.'

Why anybody should have thought of giving this lady an introduction to me is more than I can tell. I am not a gregarious person, and I know very few people in Peking. The diplomats I rarely meet, and except for a few Catholic priests, I seldom see any foreigners. Of the Americans, I only knew a few much-married missionaries, whose task in life seems to be to teach young China about George Washington and Abraham Lincoln, not to mention Jesus Christ.

In spite of these adverse circumstances, Miss Amelia Peterkin Wallace arrived at the Home of the Five Virtues and honoured me by accepting tea in my study, served Chinese fashion, without milk and sugar. She was a brisk little woman, with no pretensions to beauty and an impatient manner.

I must say this for Miss Amelia: she knew exactly what she wanted, and told me all about it, without hesitation or loss of time. She wished for two things:

First: to know what the Chinese women use to keep their hair in place. She had heard that they plastered it down with an infusion from the bark, or the wood, of a tree. But she did not know what tree. Neither did I. But we summoned the Mother of Little Lu, and the matter was soon cleared up to Miss Amelia's entire satisfaction. She went home with a sample of the wood in her satchel and precise instructions as to how it should be used.

Second: she wanted to paint a picture, representing an emperor of China (preferably of the Ming dynasty) offering up a prayer on the Altar of Heaven. I pointed out that the ceremony in question used to take place at the winter solstice, and that we were now at midsummer: the atmospheric conditions would be quite different.

Miss Amelia said she did not mind.

I asked what she wanted me to do about it.

'I want a permit to go and paint on the Altar of Heaven.'

'Better not ask for a permit. The authorities would be suspicious and might refuse. Give the door-keepers five or ten dollars to begin with, and pay them for carrying your easel and paints. As long as they make something out of it, there will be no difficulty.'

'Then I want a model.'

'What sort of a model?'

'A young man. Almost a boy. I think the picture would be more effective if the figure of the emperor were young and slim.'

'I suppose he would be standing alone?'

'Yes. In the centre of the upper terrace, and around him clouds of incense, rising.'

'Remember: it was not only incense that they burnt round the Altar of Heaven, but also the emperor's reports to the powers above, written on rolls of silk. I tell you this, because the colour of the smoke may be very different.'

'That does not matter. The smoke would be used merely to give a misty appearance to the background.'

'Well. I will do my best.'

I learnt a good deal about Miss Amelia during her stay in Peking. She derived a large income from the manufacture and the sale of a hair wash that was popular among the negroes in the southern states (hence her interest in the infusion used by Chinese women), and she spent large sums of money touring round the world and painting pictures of religious subjects, with violent effects of chiaroscuro and a scanty knowledge of perspective. I was told an irreverent story about a picture of hers, representing Christ walking on the waters. It shed an entirely new light on Our Lord's reasons for not trusting Himself to the boat.

The preparations for the picture on the Altar of Heaven started off swimmingly. Miss Amelia visited Little Li's shop in the Street of the Silks and bought a magnificent coat for the emperor to wear. We also made the necessary arrangements with the door-keepers and caretakers of the Temple of Heaven. But it was not easy to find a model. Indeed, it took so long that I began to think that the winter solstice would be upon us before we had found one to suit. In which case the atmosphere would have been historically correct.

I acted as interpreter, while Miss Amelia interviewed the candidates. They were mostly distant relatives of the Five Virtues. No one paid any attention to Miss Amelia's request to have a young man for a model. Some of the candidates might have posed for Ch'ien Lung after sixty years of reign. One young man presented himself, but his face was all swollen under his ears.

'What an object!' exclaimed Miss Amelia, when she looked him over. 'Do you think he can be ill?'

'Not very ill,' I answered, trying not to laugh. 'He is merely suffering from a slight attack of mumps.'

Miss Amelia gave a scream. 'Send him away,' she ordered. 'Are all Chinese so stupid? What possible use could I have for a model with mumps? Surely there must be some good-looking healthy boys in Peking!'

It was then that I had a brain-wave. I remembered Ur-ko.

I thought I had found a solution of the problem. And so I had. But our troubles were not yet over. Far from it.

To explain to the young goatherd what was required of him; to persuade the goatherd's parents that the foreign devils meant him no harm; to induce the door-keepers and caretakers to allow Ur-ko to stand, robed like an emperor, on the Altar of Heaven, were items in the subsequent negotiations that took much time to bring to a satisfactory conclusion. But after the disbursement of many dollars, Miss Amelia ended by getting her own way. Ur-ko, wearing a mantle of the imperial yellow, posed among clouds of incense against an evening sky.

So much having been accomplished to ensure success, it was a pity that Miss Amelia should not have possessed the necessary talent and training to produce a good picture.

The Altar of Heaven is one of the wonders of the world, not only for its intrinsic beauty, but for the grandeur of the idea that inspired its construction. It consists of a circular terrace of white marble, with a base of two hundred and forty feet in diameter, rising in three tiers from an open space in the midst of a forest of cedars. The top is a broad, round platform just a little higher than the surrounding trees, with no outlook but the broad horizon, no dome but the sky. From the centre of this platform the Son of Heaven looked up to heaven and prayed for his people. He invoked no special divinity, but the supreme powers of nature, whatever they might be.

The park of the Temple of Heaven is very extensive, and the Altar of Heaven is only one of many buildings therein. Sometimes I rode out in the evening, to see how Miss Amelia was getting on. And I liked to stand a little way off, enthralled by the beauty of the scene she was endeavouring to reproduce: the slim young figure in its glowing robes, lifting a wistful face to heaven; the marble terraces and carven balustrades, and all around the silent forest and fragrant meads.

Meanwhile, in another part of the Temple of Heaven, the pavilion known as the Chi Nien Tien had become the stage of a certain mild activity on the part of a Government Committee, which for some reason unexplained (but doubtless connected with 'squeeze'), was holding there a series of meetings, flanked by a numerous secretariat. The Chi Nien Tien is a very high building, with a triple roof of blue tiles, surrounded by a large golden 'button' or ball. The roof is visible from a great distance, and the pavilion itself forms the centre of a number of minor buildings, where in olden days they used to carry out sacrifices and ceremonies in preparation for the emperor's prayer.

From the Chi Nien Tien to the Altar of Heaven there runs a broad stone and marble causeway, raised above the forest; it is about a quarter of a mile long. The distance was such, and there were so many intervening gates and buildings, that I doubt if the activities of the Government Committee would ever have disturbed Miss Amelia at her work. But as it happened, the Committee held its meetings in the morning, whereas Miss Amelia painted only in the late afternoon. So neither knew of the other's existence. And even on the final day of its labours, when the Committee met in the afternoon amid scenes of festivity, the presence of Miss Amelia at the Altar of Heaven passed unperceived and in no way interfered with the proceedings.

I do not know for certain what the occasion was, but I gathered that foreign ministers and bank directors were invited, and that much publicity was given to a resolution to organize a great exhibition or 'World's Fair' in Peking. Such an exhibition could not fail to prove how much progress the Republic had made in its task of modernizing the country.

Since that pleasant summer's afternoon, civil wars and other troubles have relegated the exhibition to the limbo of unrealized ideals. But I believe that the meeting at the Chi Nien Tien was a great success, with rousing speeches, a gratifying enthusiasm and an excellent buffet, supplied by the Hôtel des Wagons-Lits.

I was not invited to the festival, but I went as usual to see Miss Amelia at the Altar of Heaven. I rode in under the arches, making my way with difficulty through the crowd that was pouring out, the official party having just broken up.

The temple grounds are so vast that some time elapsed before all the guests had left, and a small group of Chinese notabilities, dressed for the occasion in swallow-tail coats, top hats, and decorations, lost their way completely. Instead of taking the path through the forest of cedars, they followed the stone and marble causeway that leads from the Chi Nien Tien to the Altar of Heaven.

I noticed them when I dismounted and gave my pony to Pure Virtue to hold. Having met the crowd at the gates, I was in no way surprised to see some of the official guests walking along the causeway. But I could not help smiling at their strange appearance, in evening dress and decorations, in that place and at that hour.

The Chinese did not see me, for I was below them, half hidden among the shadows of the trees. They made their way round a low pavilion, with blue roofs and lacquered doors, where once – if what the caretakers told me is correct – the Emperor used to pass the night in fasting. Then they came out on to the path that I was following. They were some ten yards ahead of me, walking hesitatingly, as if they had begun to realize that they had taken the wrong road (or it may be that they had imbibed too much sweet champagne at the buffet).

And then a strange thing happened.

As the trees opened out and the Altar of Heaven came into view, we saw before us the figure of Ur-ko in the imperial robes, silhouetted against the sky. His arms were lifted heavenwards, as was his upturned face. Around him clouds of incense mingled with the evening mist.

The Chinese notabilities stopped dead, and for one moment, and one moment only, they gazed upon that wonderful scene. Then, as reeds before the storm, they bowed to the very ground in an irresistible impulse of adoration.

Forgotten the veneer of Western civilization, the republican ideals, the faith in a new régime! An inborn instinct, stronger than these, bade them bend their foreheads to the earth, lest their sight should profane the divine presence. For there, alone on the Altar of Heaven, stood the Son of Heaven, praying for humanity!

Half an hour later, we all walked back together: Miss Amelia and I and the Chinese notabilities. They had recovered from their surprise and showed much pleasure in meeting a distinguished American artist. One of the door-keepers of the Temple carried Miss Amelia's easel. Ur-ko, stripped of his imperial robes, ran on ahead.

High up above the blue roofs, the great golden ball of the Chi Nien Tien gathered into itself the last rays of the setting sun.

5 The Hill of the Seven Splendours

In the years before the war, Doctor Folitzky used to practise in Peking, where he was attached to the German Hospital. He was born in Prague and was a Czech, but in those days no one made distinctions between the subjects of the Hapsburg monarchy, and Dr. Folitzky was simply classed as an Austrian. I knew him well by sight, and often watched him pass noisily up the street in an old Ford of the type then known as a 'tin Lizzie'. In the year of grace 1901 he had been called in – so I was told – to assist at Kuniang's arrival in this world, but that was before I came into the story.

I met Dr. Folitzky by chance one day at the entrance of a little Chinese eating-house, where they make a speciality of turtle soup. This establishment is situated outside the Ch'ien Men, to the right, in a street whose name has for me a familiar sound, being the same as that of my domestic servants. It is called the Street of the Five Virtues, and, strangely enough, there are five houses of ill-fame in it. The turtle soup served in this modest restaurant would not be unworthy of City banquets at the Guildhall.

It is customary to go and order it the day before, choosing one's turtle (still alive) according to the size required. It is also a good plan to take one's own servant to wait at table. The waiters belonging to the house may be worthy people, but I doubt whether they ever patronize the bathing establishment, which is situated close by. I was once imprudent enough to let the house-waiter serve me. He was a pleasant-spoken young man, but when he handed me the bowl his thumb was deep in my soup, and through the liquid I could see the black new moon that was his nail.

I landed up there one rainy afternoon about three o'clock, with the object of ordering dinner for the day after. A little man with a round stomach and a pointed beard was standing before the door. He held up a Chinese umbrella made of oiled paper, from which the drops were pouring on to a small wet dog that crouched at his feet. When I drew near, I recognized Dr. Folitzky. He was cursing the dog in fluent German, but at the moment when I arrived on the scene, he changed into French and went on expressing himself with no less emphasis in that language. It was not clear what had caused his annoyance. The dog was a very ordinary Pekinese with a squashed nose and crooked legs. He was soaked with rain and looked up at his master with an apologetic expression, as if conscious of having provoked disapproval.

'Would you believe it? They sold him as a black dog!' shouted the doctor, bursting with wrath. This time he spoke in English, the *lingua franca* of the Far East.

'As black?' I inquired, not understanding what he meant.

'Yes. And moreover, he *was* black; black as coal. And now just look at him!' Here he went off into a string of expletives, more abusive than before.

I looked again at the dog. This time I understood. He had been dyed black, to give him a more uniform appearance and to enhance his value. Now, under the torrential rain, he was showing the natural colour of his coat, a sickly yellow, patched with white.

This incident served as an introduction, and as we had a common interest in turtle soup (the doctor had also come there to order a meal), we arranged to dine together.

The following evening we met there again at half-past

eight, the doctor having brought his boy, but not his dog. It did not take me long to find out that he was an indefatigable talker, though sometimes, even when in company, he had fits of abstraction, during which he remained silent, lost in his own thoughts. His conversation revealed a varied knowledge of men and things, and it passed from one subject to another like a brook over the pebbles in its bed. As soon as we were seated at table, he began to speak of the breathing apparatus of turtles and of the difficulty of respiration, caused by the inelasticity of their covering shell; also of the influence of this inelasticity on the temperament of the reptile. The doctor talked with his mouth full of a stew that he had ordered for himself. Half-way through a phrase, you would hear the broth slithering down his throat. I lost the thread of his discourse while investigating a lump of greenish meat from the carapace, or upper shell of the animal whose inelasticity of covering so much interested my companion. When I again paid attention I was surprised to hear that he was speaking about a journey to Syria.

'. . . in a village near Antioch, they pointed out to me a column, lying on the ground. It was seventy-two feet high and four wide at the top. They assured me it was the very column on which St. Simon Stylites had lived for thirty years without ever coming down. He had many imitators, the so-called Pillar Hermits. Among them was one who established himself on a column on the banks of the Bosphorus, four miles from Constantinople. But the temperature there was lower than what he had been used to. He was always catching cold. So the Emperor had a shelter placed round the column to protect him from bad weather.'

I thought it was about time I said something. So I remarked that there must have been a great deal of charlatanism in such ostentatious discomfort.

'Yes. These people were trying to prove that their minds were absorbed in religious meditation and far from terrestrial objects. If that had been the case, they would not have felt the need to *épater le bourgeois*. The most sincere of the hermits were the Persian Sufists. They were pantheistic, and their special cult, although derived from Islam, did not exclude the cult of wine. Indeed, a propensity to get drunk was considered sympathetically by the followers of Jamshid. Which reminds me. . . . The boy has not served the Madeira. One should always drink Madeira with turtle soup.'

He called his boy, who brought some Madeira in a cobwebby bottle. In the matter of eating and drinking, the doctor evidently did himself well.

'We owe the discovery of wine to Persia,' he said, as he sipped his Madeira.

'Discovery or invention?'

'Discovery. It was by chance that mankind came upon the precious liquid, just as it was by accident that Galvani discovered the electric fluid *in motu muscolari* and Bessemer found a way to make steel cheaply. Do you know the legend? No? Then I will tell it to you:

'Once upon a time, there was a concubine in the harem of the King of Persia, more beautiful and more graceful than any other woman in the kingdom. She was the king's favourite and the pride of his heart. But one day a merchant from Baghdad brought to the palace a Frankish slave-girl, whose appearance so delighted the king that he bought her forthwith and bestowed his favours upon her. The deserted concubine was so overcome with grief that she resolved on suicide. But she did not know by what means to seek death. While wandering, sad and alone, in the palace gardens, she found in a corner some amphorae full of a reddish liquid that had a bitter-sweet taste not wholly unpleasant. She hoped it might be poison and drank a cupful. The drink did not have the desired effect, so she drank a second cup, and a third. In those amphorae, left there and forgotten by the servants, was no poison but merely grape-juice which had fermented in the sun. The concubine forgot the desertion that had caused her so much sorrow, and with

62

a goblet in her hand and an amphora under her arm, she walked unsteadily to the alcove where the king reclined with his new favourite. She appeared before him with flushed face and shining eyes. "Drink, O King!" she said, "for this is the nectar of the gods and elixir of youth." The king drank, and for the first time knew the pleasure of wine.'

'Where did you get hold of that story?' I asked.

'Has it not the true flavour of the Orient? To tell the truth, I read it in an American magazine.'

'Nowadays the true flavour of the Orient is found only in American magazines, and in the *San Francisco Police Gazette*.'

The doctor smiled maliciously. 'I am told that you have started writing stories, O Maker of Heavenly Trousers!'

I stared at him. 'Why do you call me that?' I asked.

'That is how you are known in Peking. Every one here has a nickname. Yours is quite an attractive one. You have no cause to complain.'

'And what might your nickname be, if one may ask?'

'Mine could not be more impressive. I am known as Buddha come back to earth!'

'You must have effected some wonderful cures!'

'Oh, it has nothing to do with my medical practice. It is the Chinese phonetic version of my name. Folitkzy has become *Fo Li Ti*. Buddha – come – earth.'

'A name to live up to!'

'You are right. It is an inspiration in itself. Some day I may follow in the path of the Buddha and give myself to the contemplative life. Then you shall write a story about me, with the true Oriental flavour.'

The remark sounded like a jest, but I was surprised at the tone in which it was spoken. The little man might have been in earnest. And suddenly he fell into a reverie, staring straight in front of him.

I took the opportunity to observe him more closely. There was not much of the Buddha about him, save at that moment the far-away look in his eyes. He was small and plump and almost bald. His little beard and moustache gave him the look of a Frenchman, as depicted in English caricatures. His clothes were untidy and his hands were stained with chemicals.

That evening he hardly spoke any more. We had finished dinner, so we each paid our bill and went home.

In relating this conversation with Dr. Folitzky, I have reported his words in English, and in English only. But when talking to other people, as when swearing at his dog, he did not seem capable of expressing himself in less than three languages, jumping continually from one to another. I noticed also that his thought always came back to the idea of a contemplative life. When I got to know him better, I pointed out to him his own idiosyncrasies. He smiled and admitted that he might do well as hall porter in some big cosmopolitan hotel (he spoke seven languages). With regard to his favourite theme of conversation, he made an unexpected rejoinder. He began by asking if I had read Dante. I answered in the affirmative. Then he asked:

'Do you remember the Fifth Canto of the *Inferno*, the Canto of Francesca? Then you may have noticed how, when Francesca is speaking, the word *peace* recurs three times in a few lines. Peace is the antithesis to the torment of the merciless wind, *la bufera infernal che mai non resta*. The poet has observed a psychological truth: the constant return of the mind to the blessing which is lost. So in the last cantos, the souls of the damned, suffering torment in an eternal darkness, speak always of the light, *lo dolce lome*.'

'How does this apply in your case?'

'It is my ambition to follow the contemplative life, as practised in the East. It is my fate to be an overworked general practitioner. My old motor bumps me along from a birth in the Tartar City to a case of indigestion in the diplomatic quarter, and like the wind in the *Inferno* it drags my soul along with it. I would fain meditate like

64

Buddha, *jenseits Gutes und Böses*, but I must toil among the ills of the flesh and through them earn my daily bread.'

A month or two after our dinner together Dr. Folitzky disappeared from Peking. Some people attributed his disappearance to political reasons and believed it to be a proof that he was a dangerous conspirator. In Peking, as elsewhere during the War, when people did not know what to think about a man, or a woman, they accused them of being spies. The fact that the doctor had not been interned with the other 'enemy subjects' showed that his Czech nationality had been recognized as giving him the right to live in Peking undisturbed. And he had obtained (so I was told) the protection of the French Legation. Towards the end of that same year (1918) the Czech refugees began to arrive eastward out of Russia in trains hung with garlands and adorned with effigies of the Holy Grail. But I doubt if the doctor ever saw them, or ever heard of them.

I had news of him indirectly from the Chinese authorities, that is to say, from General Kuan Yu-ti, Chief of the Peking Gendarmerie.

Ever since the day when I took a photograph of General Kuan on horseback, in full uniform, with his hand on his hip, in the attitude of a *condottiere* entering a conquered city, he has honoured me with his friendship. Once a year he asks me to dinner, and at each dinner I miss some touch of the East that has disappeared, and notice some sign of the West that has come to stay. On the menus of successive years I might have studied the evolution of China towards a new form of civilization. Bird's-nest soup and stewed sharks' fins have been replaced by *Potage Parmentier* and tinned salmon from the Baltic. I am sorry. It is sad to see old customs vanish.

One of these annual dinners took place in February 1919, and it was on my arrival at his hospitable house that the General first spoke to me about a foreign recluse who had recently died on the Hill of the Seven Splendours.

Among the many official posts held by General Kuan, there was that of Sanitary Inspector of the province of Chili: a new department, characteristic of new ideas. It implied responsibility for all anti-epidemic preventive measures.

The General knows little about prophylactics and cares less. He leaves the work to a committee of doctors, and contents himself with cutting off heads of traders who persist in bringing in loads of infected wool from plague-stricken districts. He shares the Chinese popular idea that, as death must come sooner or later, it is absurd to take much trouble in order to avoid it in any particular form. Nevertheless the General has to be consulted, by virtue of his office, in all matters affecting plague prevention. This may explain why a manuscript, left by the recluse who had died on the Hill of the Seven Splendours, was placed in his hands; the plague is mentioned many times at the end of the manuscript. So the local authorities sent it up to the General, together with their own report on the manner of its discovery.

The General spoke to me about the matter during the hour before dinner that is dedicated to conversation. Although these dinners are becoming more and more Westernized, I still follow the old Chinese custom, arriving long before the time mentioned in the invitation and leaving before the last dish is served. In this manner I show a flattering haste to enjoy my host's company, and also a gratifying satiety before the supply of food is exhausted. To remain at table to the end of dinner would imply that I could still eat more.

Shorn of the preliminaries and commentaries, such as even a police report is adorned with in the Orient, the story told me by the General, during the interval between my arrival at his house and the announcement of dinner, was the following:

The head of the gendarmerie in the western City had

reported that, on the eighth day of the twelfth moon (9th of January), a hermit had died, who for some time had been leading a life of contemplation in a small temple, where the valley of Men-to-kou opens out into the plain. The temple was situated on the summit of an isolated hill overlooking the valley on one side and the plain of Peking on the other, and was known as the Hill of the Seven Splendours. The hermit was a foreigner, probably a German. He lived Chinese fashion, eating the food procured for him by the temple priest. He had no dealings with the outer world, except when he sent some one into Peking to buy wine or medicines, or when the inhabitants of the neighbouring villages came to him to be doctored. All who knew him were loud in his praise. They spoke of him as Fo Li Ti, 'Buddha come back to earth.'

He left a sheaf of papers, written shortly before he died, in a foreign language that was supposed to be German. The hermit's death had been a strange one. The small pavilion where he slept had been burnt down. It might be that he had died of asphyxiation. But the room was so small that it seemed impossible any one should have remained there, unless by chance he had been heavily drugged, or even dead, before the fire broke out.

In an outer courtyard had been found a small box. The priest, who acted as guardian to the temple, was the first to open it. He had found nothing in it but documents, though the box had an acrid smell which soon dispersed.

I asked the General if he had any theory that could explain the matter. He answered that the dead man must have been a German, who had committed suicide on hearing rumours that all German subjects were to be deported from China. The hermit preferred death to the pain of leaving the country. The General thought that I should find this theory corroborated by the manuscript. He asked me to examine it and to let him know the result. So I was given the papers, box and all.

The Chinese name, Fo Li Ti, and the mention of a

contemplative life had revealed to me that the 'hermit' must be Dr. Folitzky. This was confirmed by the contents of the box, which I took home with me after the General's dinner. The manuscript was laboriously written on sheets of rice-paper, not with a pen, but with a paint-brush in Chinese ink. On a single page, the author had expressed himself in four different languages. It became clear, as I read the manuscript, that he had no inkling, when he began to write, as to what the end of the story would be.

In putting the pages together and reducing them to one language, I had to take some liberties with the text. This could not be helped. The original manuscript was too fragmentary to be presented as a continuous whole. I have added nothing, and I have omitted only what seemed utterly irrelevant.

On that night, when we ate our turtle soup together, the doctor prophesied that some day I might write a story about him 'with the true Oriental flavour'. Except that it is he who tells the story, the prophecy has come true.

THE MANUSCRIPT OF DR. FOLITZKY

If I had books, to furnish me with data where my memory fails, I could write a treatise concerning the effects of a contemplative life on sensation and on perception. But I have no books, nor even pen and ink to write with. I string these few notes together clumsily with the aid of a paint-brush, some absorbent paper, and a cake of Chinese ink, made of lamp black and slightly perfumed, which I run down in water for use. It is true that I could send the bonze (is there such a word in English?) to procure me writing materials in Peking. But I doubt if any one could lend me the *De Vita Solitaria* and the *De Contemptu Mundi* of Petrarch, or the poem on the contemplative life by Jelal Eddin Rumi.

To take up such a work seriously, I should have to start a correspondence with librarians and scientists, read the latest publications on the hygiene of the mind, and give myself up to researches that could not be exhaustive unless I left the Hill of the Seven Splendours. To write about the contemplative life, I should have to abandon it.

I shall confine myself therefore to setting down my personal experiences, describing symptoms which I have observed in myself, not pathological symptoms, but phenomena which appear to indicate a heightening of conscious perceptive sensibility. If these notes should come into the hands of a psychologist, he may make use of the material collected. No need for me to return to the world to add one more treatise to dusty bookshelves. Better the gentle quiet of my Hill of the Seven Splendours: *Spes et Fortuna, valete – sat me lusistis.*

Concerning the relative advantages of contemplation and of action, men will always disagree, for in such arguments each of us unconsciously defends his own temperament. For my part, I used to maintain, in certain academical discussions in the past, that a life of contemplation, to be of real use, should be followed by laymen, without mystical sentimentality or religious inspiration. A man of culture and of mature intellect, seeking retirement in the intervals of an active life and enjoying the charms of silence and meditation, may find that his senses become more acute and certain mental faculties more highly developed. To a rustic, or to an ignorant man, the contrary may happen, the faculties becoming atrophied in disuse. A foundation of knowledge is necessary if the spirit is not to suffer from the absence of external stimuli. In other words, one must have resources within oneself.

This is not true of the contemplative life inspired by religion. The saving of our souls is not incompatible with the blunting of our senses. Such religions as have developed a tendency towards asceticism assume that the spiritual and material worlds are antagonistic; they praise the contemplative life, because it offers detachment. Their ideal is introspective. Saint Bernard, riding along the borders of Lake Leman, drew his hood over his face, lest his eyes should rest on the beauties of hills and sky and water.

I would give back to asceticism the meaning that it originally possessed. Among the Greeks, *askesis* meant preparation for the games, implying abstention from all that was sensual and effeminate; a hardening of the muscles, a stiffening of our powers of resistance, such as sportsmen call 'training'. In later days, the meaning of *askesis* became spiritualized, especially in the East where they associate it with the elimination of all bodily effort. This should not mean a withdrawal from nature, but a better understanding of its forces. An example is given in Kipling's story: *The Miracle of Purun Bagat*.

I suggest that, leaving aside religion, we should give to asceticism a physical significance. If practised by means of bodily exercises, it will be equivalent to a sportsman's training, but if practised in silent and, up to a certain point, in motionless contemplation, it should improve our mental faculties by giving a greater capacity of intuition. This laical idea of contemplation should consider it as a means of acquiring instinctive knowledge to be controlled and verified by experiment. Among religious people, contemplation may also be a means to an end, namely, the nearer approach of the soul to its creator. But this lies outside the field of experimental research.

My theory might be described as an intellectual quietism, and formulated as follows:

In conditions favourable to contemplation, perceptive sensibility can be developed and may overcome the limitations imposed by an active life. It is to be recommended to students as complementary to ordinary training in scientific research. A doctor will acquire knowledge in universities and experience in hospitals. A contemplative life, occasionally practised,

70

should develop the faculties of immediate apprehension by sense, and consequently the power of correct diagnosis.

The facts that I am about to set forth show the application of this theory to my own case. I begin with some biographical notes:

My name is Jasomirgott Folitzky and I was born in Prague in 1874. I took my degree in Göttingen and for two years practised under Leyden in his Klinik at Berlin. Then a great-aunt of mine died and left me enough money to satisfy the *Wanderlust* that so often assails young men. I went to Italy, where I remained two years, after which I prepared myself for a journey in the East by taking some courses at the British Institute for the Study of Tropical Diseases. I was in India at the time of the plague, and took part in the work of the Indian Plague Research Committee. I stayed there four years and then went to Burma, to Java, and at last to China, where I have made my home since 1906. By this time, only a few hundred crowns were left of my aunt's legacy, but I had acquired considerable experience and could earn my living easily enough.

I set up in medical practice in Peking and, in 1911, became a member of the Committee for the Prevention of Plague in Manchuria. This gave me the opportunity for experimental work in collaboration with Chinese and foreign doctors in Mukden. Without boasting, I may say that many of the more successful experiments were made by me. It was I who made it possible to prove that the Marmot of Manchuria (*Spermophilus citillus*) can be a bearer of contagion no less than the Siberian Tarbagàn (*Arctomys bobac*), as was first suggested by Doctor Strong.

Every two years I returned to Germany, to meet my old colleagues of the Leyden-Klinik and to learn about new discoveries in science. It was during one of these journeys that I experienced for the first time the effects on

71

myself of a contemplative life. The discovery was made by chance.

I was travelling back to China by way of Canada and had stepped off for a day or two at a place called Kenora, on Lake Winnipeg. Kenora is a summer resort, with good bathing and fishing. Although it was not yet the proper season, I was tempted to stop by some advertisements of the C.P.R. There was plenty of time to reach Vancouver and to catch my steamer for Yokohama. But the second day, when I was already getting tired of the place, I fell, while getting out of a boat, and both sprained and lacerated some muscles in my back. This meant that I had to remain lying down for nearly a month. Of course I missed the steamer on which I had reserved a cabin.

I was staying at a little country inn, kept by a Swede and his wife, on the edge of the lake. The place was deserted, as it was only April and the summer guests did not begin to arrive till May. In the daytime they carried my bed on to the veranda overlooking the lake, and I passed the time contemplating nature. That is to say: a sheet of water with floating tree-trunks, sawn into lengths and awaiting (so I imagine) to be loaded on to trains; in the distance the fir woods and their reflection in the lake; a landing-stage where steamers came in the summer, but which was now abandoned; an occasional bird, poised on the floating lumber; a fish rising to a fly and the widening circles after the splash; the shadows lengthening at sunset; the stars coming out just as I was carried into the house, and that was all! Nothing to read. The two old Swedes could offer me only the boot and shoe catalogue of a Chicago firm, and the time-table of the C.P.R. which I studied for hours, reading the queer names of stations (I remember there was one called 'Bonheur'). All day long there was nothing to do but to gaze and to think, to think and to gaze. Yet after the first few days of pain and utter boredom, there followed a period of mental calm, such as I had never experienced before. This calm brought with it an abnormal mental lucidity. A doctor's existence is necessarily agitated, especially if he be a general practitioner. Though he should maintain a tranquil manner towards his patients, it is a serenity enforced from within, despite disturbing circumstances. At Kenora nothing happened to distract or to disturb me, except one most insignificant episode, which served to reveal the effect of enforced immobility upon my faculties.

The old woman who ran the inn did all the housework, for in that season it did not pay to keep a help. Her husband assisted her as best he could, for she was in bad health. She had a weak stomach. One day, while she was putting my room in order, she told me that shortly before my arrival she had been to see a doctor at Moose Jaw, and he had given her some medicine. The old woman did not consult me about her ailment, thinking possibly that I could hardly be a professional medical man, as I took so long to cure my own back. I asked her if the medicine given her by the doctor at Moose Jaw had done her any good. She said not.

'Probably your teeth are out of order. You do not masticate properly. Go and see a dentist.'

I expressed this opinion and gave the advice casually, almost without thinking. The old woman thanked me in a manner no less casual, while she busied herself about the room. She said it was true that her teeth gave her trouble. During the summer, when a dentist came to Kenora, she would consult him.

Later in the day, thinking over what I had said, I felt puzzled at a feeling of absolute certainty as to the correctness of my diagnosis. I could not have felt more sure of myself after the most careful examination.

A few days later I was able to leave Kenora. Several times, during the journey by train and while stopping at Vancouver, I watched my fellow-travellers and I had a feeling as of divining power. I knew by instinct what ills they suffered from. Several times I was able to verify the accuracy of my intuition. Had I been occupied with professional diagnosis in those days, I might have accomplished miracles. But in time this exceptional discriminative faculty disappeared.

Now it has come back to me, on the Hill of the Seven Splendours.

These poor people in a Chinese village have among them a healer such as even Leyden never was (and in Berlin they considered him the greatest physician of our age). Save that my powers can cure only the ills of the body, and offer no alleviation from the sufferings of the soul, I almost deserve my name of Buddha come back to earth!

Sometimes I feel that I should let the world know, so that all might come and be cured. But that would mean giving up the contemplative life. And then my healing powers might wane and disappear.

Before entering into particulars concerning my medical experience in these surroundings, it may be well to give some idea of the place itself and of the life I lead.

The temple which has become my *buen retiro* crowns a little hill about three hundred feet high, rising solitary in the midst of the plain. In the distance are visible, when the air is clear, the bowmen's towers that rise above the gates of Peking. In the opposite direction, that is to say, towards the north-west, opens out the valley of Men-to-kou, and down it flows the river which circles round this hill of mine. Below me, and so close that from my terrace I can look into the courtyards of the houses, is a village. Near it is a group of trees (cedars, willows, and limes), and in their shadow a row of tombs.

Though I retired from Peking less than a year ago, I feel as if I had been here all my life (it is true that I came here occasionally even before). The inhabitants of my village – I call it mine, having grown fond of it – are all known to me by sight. I also know the age of the children and can tell with precision when others will be born. I can guess how long the coal will last, that is brought on the backs of camels from Men-to-kou, and when the Merry Widow will have her next funeral.

The Merry Widow's real name is Sing Tai-tai and her funeral takes place once every three months. This is because she has quarrelled with her relations and fears that, when she dies, they will not give her a proper funeral and observe all the prescribed rites. She directs the procession from a neighbouring hillock and volubly abuses the priests and the bearers. Her villa is the one fine habitation in this locality. Its courtyards are open to my gaze. The one nearest the entrance is adorned, during the summer, by two rows of earthenware pots containing lotus plants. Between the pots are tall perches and on each perch is a parrot. There are eight of them, and they make more noise than the *Vogelhaus* in Hamburg.

The villa where the Merry Widow lives was once a prison. A certain prefect of Honan, whose peculations had been a little too flagrant, was imprisoned there. The premises were not to his liking, and, being a man of means, he had the old prison knocked down and a new one built in its stead, or, in other words, a villa, where he continued his confinement in great luxury. Thus the Imperial Edict, which relegated him to that spot, was duly observed without discomfort to the prisoner. History does not say what happened to the other jail-birds. Possibly they accepted situations as servants to their more powerful colleague.

The Merry Widow, by the way, is one of my patients. She suffers from excessive blood-pressure. I have had to warn her against losing her temper on the occasions of her periodical interments. If she is not careful, some day she will have a fit and die. Then she won't have any more funerals!

A most delightful contemplation is that which has running water for its material focus: a river, a torrent, a stream. The river that flows below me, winding south-wards, is too distant to offer the restful sight of moving waters. It forms part of a greater panorama, of a picture that remains the same throughout the centuries, yet changes from day to day and from hour to hour. In the variety of light and shade and colours, I find compensation for the distractions that I gave up when I gave up a life of activity.

In the winter the river is frozen and gleams whitely, like the pebbles on either bank. In summer it is blue or green, according to its depth, and those cool shades are restful to the eye amidst the glare of the stony banks. Downstream, on the far edge of the horizon, I can just distinguish the many-arched bridge of Pu-li-san-ghin, described by Marco Polo.

The pavilion where I live is the highest of a group of similar buildings, which climb the southern slope of the hill. It does not rise to the very top, but leans against the summit, so as to be protected from the north wind. From my terrace (two yards wide by six long) one looks out over the roof of the pavilion below, which is uninhabited. There are statues there of painted wood, representing Buddhist sages.

Farther down are the bonzes. There are two of them. One is a young man who fulfils the duties of village priest. The other, judging by his appearance, must be of an incredible age. He also follows the contemplative life, never moving out of his cell, where he sits with crossed legs and eyes fixed in front of him, absorbed in medi-tation. Every now and then I hear his querulous voice complaining because the rice they bring him is too much, or not sufficiently cooked. In his case, detachment from worldly matters cannot be as complete as he makes out.

I do not pretend, as he does, to see nothing of what is in front of me. At one time I used to go for walks in the hills, or took a gun to shoot snipe in the marshes to the east. But it is a long time, now, since I have been down in the plain. In winter I sit in the sun, in some sheltered spot, and in summer I stay on my terrace, or in a half-darkened room, with a Japanese portière to keep the flies out.

I have mentioned my terrace, but there are two, and I pass from one to the other, according to the season or the direction of the wind. They are both on the same level. One almost overhangs the village, and the other looks out over the river. From the first, I watch the human drama; from the other I contemplate the pageant of nature.

Though other voices reach my ear, I am silent. A word of thanks when they bring me my food is sometimes all the conversation I indulge in for days together. When people come for medical advice, my questions are few and my instructions brief. Thus I inspire greater confidence. My patients like to think that the diagnosis is based on a supernatural sense of divination, rather than on indecorous medical examinations. And so it should be, for healing is one of the attributes of divinity. Chinese women (unless they have been brought up by foreign missionaries) will not uncover themselves even for a doctor. But I have brought with me one of those little ivory figures that Chinese physicians use, representing a naked woman, lying on her side (as if sick, in bed). My female patients point out to me, on this little figure, the place where they feel a pain.

But such aids to diagnosis are of little use, and it is fortunate that a contemplative life has increased my powers of intuition. I can almost feel the cause of another person's illness by a reflected physical sympathy.

I keep a small dispensing pharmacy of my own, but when necessary I write a prescription, and my patients take it into Peking. The assistants of the German pharmacy in the Hata Men are among the few people who know of my existence out here. Sometimes the younger bonze goes to town to get me something I need: cartridges, or wine, or medicines. But this happens seldom; my wants grow fewer as time passes. My one amusement, now, is to scour the plain with my field-glass, and sometimes I have a shot at a heron, on the banks of the river. For this, I use a Mannlicher-Schönhauer rifle, with telescope attachment.

As I said before, I have no books, and I never see a newspaper.

Up to this point, the style of Dr. Folitzky's manuscript, as also the handwriting, reveals the author's serenity of spirit. The writer feels that he has much time ahead; he lingers over descriptions that have nothing to do with his principal theme. Although a paint-brush is used instead of a pen, the writing is clear.

But from now onward, everything is changed; the style becomes hurried, almost telegraphic; articles and prepositions are missing. The writer is in haste, in desperate haste. . . . He must finish before something happens, something that he fears but cannot avoid. The handwriting is almost illegible. Many words are abbreviated.

February the 24th, 1919
I had intended, at this point, to insert some notes about my diagnosis of various cases of sickness, in order to demonstrate the improvement of my intuitive faculties in the tranquillity of a contemplative life. But now there is no time. Three days ago, in the evening, I was standing on the terrace that overlooks the river, searching through my glasses for a heron. Being of the same colour as the stones, they are not easy to see.

On the other side of the river, a Chinese woman was coming down the path from the hills. She was walking slowly, and every now and then she paused to rest. She drew near the ford; that is to say, to the place where, in summer-time, one can ford the river. At this season one can walk across the ice.

The sun was setting behind the Western Hills.

Quite by chance, I sighted the woman through my

field-glass and stopped for a moment to look at her. As I did so, I felt a sudden overwhelming impulse of fear, and my hand trembled. Although she walked as any weary person might walk, even with normal feet (whereas her feet were bound), I had the impression that she was ill. That was nothing to cause surprise. China must be full of sick women, travelling alone and on foot. But I felt that in the solitary figure, slowly and painfully advancing towards the ford, there was something sinister, something menacing.

Those who live in the East well know the haunting fear of the plague, especially of the pneumonic plague, of which every case is fatal. And the horror of its drawing nearer and nearer, across a continent, from province to province, through village after village. . . . And the knowledge that you cannot stop it, any more than you can stop the shadow of a cloud that moves across the plain!

I had the impression, nay, I *knew*, that this woman had the plague.

And she was coming . . .

She was coming to my village, carrying the contagion.

My rifle was loaded and ready at hand in case I saw a heron. I took it up and fired twice at the woman. The first shot missed her. At the second, she fell and lay there on the pebbles, close to the river-bed. I think she must have died within an hour.

No one noticed what I had done. They are used to hearing my rifle.

After twenty minutes or more, the sun disappeared behind the hills.

During the night I went down to bury her. It was an arduous task, for the ground was as hard as iron. The cold was intense, and my hands were frozen. I well knew the risk I ran in burying that body. It was thus that the contagion spread in Manchuria. But what could I do?

Now I know that I have caught the infection. I must take care, in dying, not to give it to others. I have still a few hours left. There is just time to take the necessary precautions.

It is a pity. My work had just begun. And I was happy here, on my Hill of the Seven Splendours.

Iste terrarum mihi super omnes angulus ridet.

(End of the manuscript)

I have always thought what a loss to the world was the death of Dr. Folitzky, unknown and unremembered, in the little Chinese village, within sight of Peking.

Not that I believe in his theory concerning the contemplative life. That was evolved from his own nature and experience. He was a nervous man, and his incessant talk when in company was a symptom of his nervousness. He was garrulous in self-defence. Only when alone and at rest, that is to say, when his nerves were soothed by the tranquillity of his surroundings, could he exercise his truly remarkable gift of intuition. The immediate insight, surprising even to himself, was possible only when he was not worried by the anxieties of his everyday life.

But think what remarkable healing powers the man must have had, when he lived on the Hill of the Seven Splendours! For he was convinced of his own capacity to cure. Such a conviction carries with it all the thaumaturgic powers of hypnotic suggestion. And then the mystic appeal of his name and his surroundings! A good publicity agent might have turned him into a paying concern in no time. A secretary's office down in the village; a press bureau in Peking with correspondents in New York, London, and Paris, and we might have had sick millionaires from all the world over, waiting their turn to go up and be cured by Buddha come back to earth! And even without such adventitious aids to wealth and notoriety, if he had merely lived on as a healer on the Hill of the Seven Splendours, in time his fame would have spread all over Asia. He would have become a legend;

80

perhaps even the founder of a new religion. Such things have happened before.

We never found out if the woman really had the plague, and if he contracted the disease in burying her. To ascertain whether his vaunted intuition had been correct, a post-mortem examination would have been necessary. But General Kuan was not inclined to take trouble. All I can say is that there was plague in North China at that time, and it raged in the provinces outside the Wall. Many died at Kalgan and in the villages round Nankow.

After reading the manuscript, I went to see the Hill of the Seven Splendours. It was easy to recognize the places mentioned in the minute description. In a court-yard of the temple I was met by the little dog that the doctor had bought, thinking it was black, till its colour washed off in the rain. It had grown old and was blind of one eye. Strange that it was never mentioned in the manuscript!

The priests sold me a picture, painted by a local artist, in which the features of the poor doctor were idealized so that they became those of the Buddha. The painter had given him a halo and a sceptre, and placed him on a throne, before which were globes of fire, a sacramental vase, and two dwarf pines.

As I stood on the sunny terrace and looked down on the village and across the plain towards Peking, my eye fell on a procession moving westward. Green and scarlet figures carried a heavy catafalque and waved banners in the air. Every now and then a handful of gilded disks were tossed up into the spring sunshine and fell back to earth. The weird note of a *lituus* was borne to me on the breeze.

From a hillock near by, a little group of women watched the procession pass. There was an old lady among them, richly dressed, who from time to time gave orders and shouted words that sounded like abuse. I could not help smiling as I recognized the Merry Widow, directing the ceremonies of her own funeral.

6   Sacred and Profane Love

'. . . *talium est enim regnum coelorum.*' ST. MATT.
xiv. 19.

I sometimes think that the name 'Little Friend of all the
World', given to Kim in Kipling's story, might also be
applied to Kuniang. She has a knack of making friends
with all and sundry: animals and men and gods. Yes,
even gods, as I will prove in the following pages! Most of
these friendships date from her childhood, when she
frequented the convent school. I believe that no less than
seventeen different nationalities were represented in
her class. The number was made up of Asiatics as well
as of Europeans and Americans: pupils with white skins,
and brown and black; some with round eyes and some
with eyes that slanted. Together with the children of the
German chemist in the Hata Men, of the Indian silk merchant in Morrison Street and of the Swiss watchmaker
opposite the American Legation Guard, there were two
little Mongolian princesses, a Korean, several Manchus, a few Chinese, Annamites and Siamese, as well as
children from the foreign Legations. And Kuniang made
friends with them all.

How it could be possible to impart a uniform tuition to
such a heterogeneous crowd I cannot imagine. Some
must have required to be dragged forward and some
back. As soon as each child left the schoolhouse, after
lesson time, it lapsed into its own national surroundings.
The only language (if such it can be called) that they had

in common was a mixture of pidgin English and Chinese. In this jargon, Kuniang would have long conversations with a little Portuguese girl from Macao, the Mongolian princesses and the daughter of the Italian Chargé d'Affaires. The pupils seemed all perfectly happy, and Kuniang was devoted to Sister Chiara.

Later on, when she went daily to the Russian family, she met the varied collection of their friends. In the summer-time they used to congregate at the swimming pool that Patushka had made in his garden; and they all bathed there together in the costume of Eden before the fall. They must have got to know each other quite well.

The Five Virtues have numerous connections who seem to know Kuniang of old, and she herself has cronies in the most unexpected places.

This being the case, I was not surprised when, coming into the house a few days ago, I noticed a yellow-robed lama, with a shaven head, sitting in the *k'ai-men-ti's* lodge. When I inquired what he wanted, I was told that he was waiting to see Kuniang. He came from the Lama Temple, which is at the other end of the town. The Five Virtues, who seemed to know all about him, offered him tea.

I myself have some friends among the lama priests, but I had never heard of Kuniang knowing any. Their Temple is miles away from where we live. The priest, whom I saw waiting in the *k'ai-men-ti's* lodge, was a very young man, hardly out of his teens. Later on, I asked Kuniang who he was.

'That is Baldàn,' she answered. 'He is a very old friend. I knew him when he first became a monk.'

'Then it cannot be very long ago.'

'Ten or twelve years; perhaps more.'

'But hang it all! You must have been a child at the time, and so must he!'

'So we were. Baldàn gave up tending his father's flocks and became a *ch'ela* when he was not yet ten years old. He told me all about it. He shaved his head, put on a yellow robe and took service with an older monk, who in his turn was the disciple of one older still, who served the Living Buddha. Baldàn is the seventh of eleven children, and four of his brothers are monks, as he is.'

'The result of economic pressure, in a country that lives on its pastures. Where does he come from?'

'Somewhere near Urga, though I believe his native village moves about according to the season. You see, they are nomads and live in huts all made of felt, which can be taken to pieces and set up again elsewhere.'

'Still, I don't understand how you got to know him.'

'That was when he first came to Peking. We got into an awful scrape together. It was my fault, really.'

'I can well believe it. What did you do?'

'It is a long story. Are you sure you want to know?'

'Of course I do. I love to hear episodes of your lurid past. When did it happen?'

'In the old days, when I lived down the street with Papà, only he was never there. And I used to come here to play in the courtyards with Little Lu. One day I came as usual and I found that the Five Virtues were taking advantage of your being away in the Western Hills, to go and see the Devil's Dance at the Lama Temple. They were taking Little Lu, and lots of food to eat while they were there.'

'I suppose you asked them to take you along.'

'That is exactly what I did do. And they said Yes, and got out an old fur-lined leather jacket of yours to wrap me up in, for it was very cold: just after the Chinese New Year. And we had to go in rickshaws.'

'Did they give you my best fur rug to wrap your legs in?'

'I don't think it was your best one, but they certainly wrapped me up very well, and tied a silk handkerchief round my head to keep my ears warm. Little Lu and I shared a rickshaw between us. We were very snug.'

'I can see your faces, peering out over the top of the rug, thoroughly happy!'

'Yes. It was great fun. Chinese love an excursion, and they always lug the children along too. You would have thought that Little Lu was much too small for a long day's outing in the middle of winter, but he behaved like a perfect lamb and gave far less trouble than I did.'

'Again I can well believe it. What happened when you got there?'

'We went into the central pavilion, where there was some sort of ceremony going on, with lots of incense, and droning prayer, and beating of drums. The Living Buddha sat on a throne at the back of the hall, with the dark shadows behind him. And he looked down at us.'

'Are you sure it was the Living Buddha? He does not often come to Peking.'

'I know it was. He was here on a visit. And the priests of the Yellow Religion had come to the Lama Temple from all over Asia to meet him. He looked so grand on his lacquer throne, with a halo of flames behind him, and clouds of incense smoke at his feet.'

'What do you mean: a halo of flames? Not real flames, surely?'

'No, gilded wood. A leaf-shaped halo with the point upwards, like they put behind the statues of the Buddha. The hall and the robes were all gold and yellow and orange.'

'What a subject for Veronese, or Turner! And what did the ceremony consist of?'

'I was too small to understand. The priests sat on benches along the sides of the hall; three rows of them on each side. The oldest priests at the back, and the youngest towards the middle. These were little boys, some of them not any older than I; all dressed in yellow robes, with a fold of rust-colour across the chest, and wonderful plumed hats, all yellow.

'Exalted Virtue and Little Lu and I stood near the end of one of the benches, where the youngest of the priests were. I was very envious, for each priest had a small drum stuck on the end of a stick. Three or four short strings hung from the side of the drum, with brass pellets at the end. When they twirled the stick, these little brass balls hit the drum and made a terrific row. They did this in the pauses between the prayers. A sort of Amen, I think.'

'I suppose so. And you wanted to join in?'

'Yes. I asked the little boy priest nearest to me if he would not let me twirl the drum for him next time. But he refused and looked very cross. That was Baldàn, the priest you saw here to-day.'

'Just like you, Kuniang, to want to officiate in a Buddhist religious ceremony. No wonder the poor boy was shocked!'

'He got a worse shock in a few minutes. Next time the prayer died away, I grabbed his drum off the low table where he had laid it, and I twirled it like anything. I made more noise than any one else. The thing was like a gigantic rattle. It was great fun!'

'Were you not turned out of the temple, like the money-changers in the New Testament?'

'Yes, I was!'

'The Five Virtues must have lost face horribly. But still I don't see how you came to make friends with Baldàn. He can't have been pleased with you either.'

'No. But I met him again later in the day, and we made it up. We got quite fond of each other.'

'Such are the wiles of women! How did you manage to seduce him?'

'Well, after the ceremony indoors, there came the Devil's Dance in the biggest of the courtyards. You know what these Chinese ceremonies are! It was supposed to start in the morning, but at half-past three in the afternoon they had not yet begun. There was a great crowd, and hardly any space left in the middle of the courtyard for the priests to dance in. Curiously enough, it was the elder priests who danced, wearing great masks in the shape of stags' heads, or wild boar, or devils. The younger priests were supposed to represent spectators, sitting on a yellow carpet and wearing shiny white masks that smiled. Baldàn was one of these. But he was quite small. Like me, he was only nine years old. The real spectators, the ones without masks, soon crowded him out, with all the other boy monks.

'I waited about for a long time. But in the end I got tired, and my feet were like ice. Only the Chinese never seem to get sick of waiting. I am sure that the Five Virtues would have stood there for days and not complained.

'They never noticed when I wandered off by myself. I entered the pavilion where there is the great gilded Buddha, the one whose head almost touches the roof. The air was heavy with incense, so that one could only see up as far as the Buddha's hands. And there I found Baldàn, sitting on the floor, all alone.'

'I suppose you immediately began to flirt with him.'

'You might call it that. I had some chocolates in my pocket and I offered him one. He did not know what to do with it, for it was wrapped up in silver paper. I took out another, and unwrapped it and ate it, to show him how.'

'And that was the beginning of his downfall. The woman tempted me and I did eat.'

'Next, I tried on his white mask and his embroidered coat.'

'Didn't he object?'

'He did not mind, as long as we remained there, in the pavilion of the big Buddha. But I wanted to go and show myself to Little Lu and the Five Virtues. I thought it would give them the surprise of their lives, if I went up to them dressed like that, and then took off my mask.'

'You certainly seem to have entered into the spirit of the Devil's Dance. What happened then?'

'I went out again into the open air, though Baldàn tried to stop me. He was terrified.'

'No wonder! A woman's passion for dressing up should stop short of sacerdotal vestments. And so that is how you got him into trouble?'

'There was no trouble, really. Only that, with the white mask on my head, I could not see where I was going. Soon I found a carpet under my feet, and I followed that through a door and into a room. Then I heard a gasp from Baldàn, and I guessed that something must be wrong. So I took the mask off, to see where I was.'

Kuniang smiled as if at an amusing recollection. Then she went on:

'We had entered a small, bare room, with no furniture in it at all, a sort of cell. There was only one person in it, sitting cross-legged on the floor. I recognized the little man who had occupied the throne during the ceremony in the early morning.'

'The Living Buddha!'

'Yes. And Baldàn seemed horribly frightened. I could not see why. The little man looked so fragile and so quiet. His face was kind and gentle and wise. He had a bowl of rice beside him and a cup of water. There was nothing imposing in his surroundings; nothing except the coat that rested on his shoulders and enveloped his figure, spreading out on the floor beside him. It was of brown satin, lined with sables, with huge buckles of turquoise set in gold. When I looked at him, he smiled and made a sign to me to come and sit at his feet.'

'Did you?'

'Yes. And when he got over his fright Baldàn came too. We sat there together, with the white mask on the floor beside us. The room was cold, so the Buddha took a fold of his coat and put it round us. You have no idea how soft it was, or how warm.'

'Did he speak to you?'

'No. He said nothing. After the first moments he did not even look at us. Do you know? I felt that there was really something God-like about him.'

'And like the living God of another religion, he suffered little children to come unto him.'

'But the Five Virtues got an awful fright!'

'Why? Because they had lost you?'

'Yes. And they only found me again when everything was over and the crowd had gone home.'

'But why did you not join them before? You seem to have been very naughty that afternoon.'

'I was tired, and so was Baldàn. When they found us, we were fast asleep, wrapped in the sable coat, and the Buddha keeping watch.'

So that is how Kuniang and Baldàn first made friends. They have remained so ever since.

It makes a pretty picture – does it not? – the Living Buddha with the two children asleep in the folds of his sable coat. And at their feet the white mask smiling.

Interlude

Stories of Kuniang's past, dating like that of Baldàn from the years of her childhood, and others from the days before we were married, reach my ears from time to time, and they make me regret that I had not heard them when I was writing *The Maker of Heavenly Trousers*. My book might have been more vivid. And it might have been a little different if I had had access to her diaries – those diaries that are now kept with the other manuscripts in my old metal dispatch-box.

Most girls begin a diary about once a year and write up the first few days with an enthusiasm that gradually wanes. Kuniang has kept it up till 'present day'. The dates are those of the lunar calendar and the English is interpersed with Chinese words and phrases (in some cases I have inserted a translation in brackets).

I am called King Cophetua in these diaries. Kuniang looked upon herself as the Beggar Maid.

She has now consented to the publication of a few extracts. And so, for the benefit of those who have not read the *Heavenly Trousers*, I must explain that when she was quite small Kuniang lived close by with her father, Signor Cante, who was an Italian engineer employed on the Kin Han railway. They occupied the top floor of an absurd house with pink walls and a clock tower. She was eight years old when she first ran into my garden after her white kitten. The Five Virtues were kind to her and asked her to come again, which she did every day, after returning home from the convent school near the Legation Quarter. Exalted Virtue, my number one boy, and the Mother of Little Lu, his wife, practically looked after her for years (the story of the picnic to the Lama Temple dates from this period in Kuniang's life). Her own mother died when Kuniang was seven, and her father was nearly always away at his job on the railway.

They pulled down the house with the clock tower when Kuniang was alone in Peking (Signor Cante, as usual was in Honan) and Exalted Virtue suggested that I should offer the child a refuge in the Shuang Liè Ssè. I was delighted to do so, for I liked to see Kuniang running about the place. So permission was granted and she was given a pavilion all to herself.

That was the beginning of our story.

The first batch of extracts from her diary is taken from a copy-book, to which she confided her experiences when she was seventeen years old. She had left the convent school and went daily for 'lessons' to a Russian family that lived near by. The father, like Signor Cante, was an employee of the Kin Han. They were musical people, and their singing, even though they did not possess very good voices, was a joy for ever. The boy, Fédor, had a talent for drawing, which constituted his principal interest in life. He drew portraits of his friends in and out of season.

I thought, at the time, that Kuniang should never have been entrusted to such people. They were a disreputable crew, though amusing to the onlooker. In the end I had to interfere and take Kuniang away from them. But she maintains that I never understood the Russian family. They often gave her a rotten time (so she says), but for thrills, pleasant or otherwise, no one could beat them. And thrills, even unpleasant ones, are better than dullness.

When Signor Cante sent her to them for tuition, Kuniang knew what to expect, and she faced the prospect with equanimity. She and the Russian children were about the same age and had been chums ever since they were quite small. The father and mother, Patushka and Matushka, were rather like children themselves, vague and absent-minded; gentle and kind as a rule, but subject to sulks and to fits of jealousy. When in a bad humour, they would vent their feelings on any one who happened to be round at the time.

The nuns of the convent school had tried to inspire in their pupils an almost bashful modesty. The Russian family went gaily to the other extreme. Nudism had not yet been heard of in China, but they made a cult of it. For the discipline of their own son and daughter, almost to the age of twenty, the parents favoured an old-fashioned instrument of punishment, made of carefully selected birch twigs. And they used it also on Kuniang. She did not complain. She never was one to complain.

There is no need here to go into the discrepancies between Kuniang's diary and *The Maker of Heavenly Trousers*. If the reader is acquainted with the former book, he will notice them for himself. One circumstance may strike him, as it struck me, namely, that the boy, Fédor, was a much more complicated character than I realized in those days. But, then, Kuniang, who had strict injunctions from her father never to 'bother' me, carefully abstained from telling me things that might have made me more anxious about her and more disapproving of the Russian family than I already was.

7   Kuniang's Diary

Seventeenth Day of the Eighth Moon

A strong wind, but no dust as the ground is sodden with rain. Fédor and Natasha brought their kites to the open plot of ground near here. The kites have bamboo whistles attached to them, each with two notes. They make a humming noise when in the air. I watched them for some time this afternoon.

A flock of pigeons came over the Tartar Wall and wheeled round, going at a great pace. Some of the pigeons also had bamboo whistles fastened on to their tails, and they all hummed together, like a deep chord on an organ, 'way up in the sky.

Fédor had brought a friend of his, a Russian boy called Igor. He is always round their house in these days, and Fédor uses him as a model. Igor is wonderfully good-looking, with curly hair and a complexion like a girl's, but he strikes me as being half daft. At any rate, he is even more vague and moony than the rest of them.

Igor is inclined to make love to me, but as I only speak a few words of Russian, we have to talk in Chinese. And Chinese is not a good language to make love in. At least, I do not find it so. You seem to get to the point at once. And then what? Either you get married or something, or nothing happens.

Second Day of the Seventh Moon

Little Lu was full of gossip to-day. He says that his aunt (Pure Virtue's wife) conceived a son last night. I asked him how he could be sure of that. Little Lu said his grandmother arranged it all. She went yesterday (first day of the new moon) to the Niang Niang Miao (the Old Woman's temple) and brought away a clay baby. She gave this to Pure Virtue, who tied a red ribbon round its neck and took it home. So that's all right!

Pure Virtue has been married more than a year, and still no signs of a baby. Which is tiresome, as he never could afford a concubine.

Thirteenth Day of the Ninth Moon

Han-lu: 'cold dew'.

The stoves are being put up for the winter, and the window frames are being gone over and repaired.

King Cophetua does not often lose his temper, but this afternoon I saw the old coolie with the pigtail flying for his life in the direction of the *k'ai-men-ti's* lodge.

What had happened was that the coolie had been told to go round and fill up the cracks in the window frames with tow, and to be careful and do them *all*. He took this to mean that, when there was no crack to fill up, he should make one with his knife. King Cophetua found him doing this in his study. There was a fine row!

Thirteenth Day of the Tenth Moon

Beginning of winter.

My old goatskin coat is wearing out and it is now so short that my thighs get chapped in the cold weather. I hardly like to go in a rickshaw for the air that blows up under my skirt.

After I had come home from the Russian family to-day I went round to the stables, and there I met King Cophetua going out through the Gate of Happy Sparrows. He was carrying something in a newspaper and when he saw me he started and looked guilty, as if I had caught him doing something wrong. But he stopped to explain that he was going out to feed a poor lady *wonk* with a litter of puppies, in the ditch under the Tartar Wall.

I asked him why he did not go out through the main entrance, and he said that he did not want the Five Virtues to see him. 'I have always told them not to encourage wonks about the place!'

'And what have you got in that newspaper?'

'Bread and bones and meat; the remains of my lunch. I have to stay with the poor brute while she eats it, or some beggar or coolie would take it away from her. A big town is a cruel thing.'

'Have you been feeding her long?'

'About ten days. It is not usual for them to have puppies at this season. I doubt if they can live through the great cold.'

I think that King Cophetua must be the kindest man in the world. But he does not want it known.

Twenty-seventh Day of the Tenth Moon

Hsiao hsueh: 'slight snow'.

Very cold. Little Lu is now wearing two quilted coats, one on top of the other.

Yesterday I did not feel like going to the Russian family and I sent the *tingchai* round to say I was not coming. This morning, when I went there, I got a fine fright, for Natasha told me that her mother was very angry and I was certainly in for trouble.

Luckily I managed to explain. It was all the *tingchai's* fault. He had given my message all wrong. What can you expect when he stammers so that one can hardly make out what he says? Half the time he is away on his errands is spent stuttering and sputtering in painful attempts to pronounce his words. King Cophetua gave him the job out of charity. His grandfather is caretaker somewhere in the Summer Palace, and has to keep a large family with two wives and several old mothers (secondary wives of his father) on three dollars a month.

The old *tingchai* was much better. I wish he had not left. But I believe he is making lots of money out of blackmail.

And this new boy looks such a scarecrow! Some days ago he appeared in a green flannel dressing-gown of foreign make and a bowler hat. He had bought them at night at the Thieves' Market outside the Hata Men. The dressing-gown trails behind him in the dust and the bowler hat comes down over his ears. But he is convinced that he is correctly attired for service in a foreign household. The Five Virtues do not seem to think it matters, and King Cophetua only laughs!

But I won't send him messages to the Russian family again.

Thirteenth Day of the Eleventh Moon

Ta hsueh: 'great snow'. But of course still no snow. Only another drop in the temperature. Little Lu has put on yet another quilted coat.

Fédor is busy painting paper gods: I mean saints. There are lots of Russians here, who want to buy them, as well as Chinese who have been converted to the Greek Church. Even after they have become Christian, the Chinese hanker after the old paper gods that they paste up all over the place at the *Kuo Nien*, the crossing of the year. Fédor says that the Greek bishop used to have paper pictures sent out from Russia, to distribute. But since the war began they don't sell them any more. So Fédor paints them and sells them. But they are much too good, really.

The ones I like best are a Nativity, with the three kings dressed up like Chinese emperors of the Ming dynasty. And Saint Nicholas, and Theodor and Anthony. He has given Saint Anthony the face of young Igor, and my face to Saint Olga.

Fédor has made me a present of a wooden plaque, carved and painted by himself: an ikon. It represents the head of Christ, wearing a crown of thorns, with jewels shining among the thorns. It is a lovely thing. I showed it to King Cophetua, who was quite astonished. He said, 'I never knew the young scoundrel had so much talent or good taste.'

The whole Russian family are going on an expedition to the Western Hills, where there is a small Russian colony. Once there used to be a real Russian village there, only it was destroyed during the Boxer troubles and most of the inhabitants killed. Patushka explained to me that it was a Siberian village, brought to Peking from the banks of the Amur, with church, houses, furniture, people, children, cattle, dogs, cats, and bugs, all complete. This was because the Chinese emperor K'ang-hsi wanted to see what a foreign village looked like.

The name of the village was Albazin.

Fourteenth Day of the Eleventh Moon

At the last moment Matushka discovered that there was room for me in the hired motor-car that was to take them to the Western Hills. That is to say, she discovered that the car had only one chauffeur. Most hired cars in Peking have two: one to drive and the other to show him how to do it. So I was taken along in the spare seat. It was great fun, though we were awfully crowded: Patushka and Matushka and Fédor and Natasha, and Igor, besides myself and the chauffeur. A fine day. Cold but still.

There was not much left of the village of Albazin; just a stairway up the hill-side and a bell-tower and a few huts. But there were three bells still hanging in the tower, and they had a double-headed eagle on them and a shield with what Patushka says are the arms of the Tsar.

About thirty Russians had come out, like us, from Peking. Only two or three live in the huts. One of these was a big, burly man, in high boots that looked as if they were made of wood. He showed Patushka the skins of animals he had killed, or trapped, in the hills; mostly cats, but there were some skins of badgers.

By climbing a little farther up the hill, one could see the sunlight reflected on the frozen lakes of the Summer Palace. As the sun began to go down, it grew very cold. We went and sat in one of the huts, in a long bare room, all dust and cobwebs, and we were given little glasses of vodka and tea out of a samovar. Everybody smoked cigarettes, and as there were only a few chairs, most of us sat on the floor.

A tall slim man in a military coat and a grey astrakhan cap stood at the end of the room and talked. The only light came from two lanterns at his feet. It cast distorted shadows on the wall and ceiling, but left the speaker's face in darkness. He was telling about what was happening in Russia and Siberia. Once he quoted a Chinese proverb: 'All the stars in heaven salute the north!'

I could understand a little of what he said. He was comparing Russia to China. Here the empire has fallen. There is no Son of Heaven to pray on the Altar of Heaven. And the days of Tsardom are counted in Russia. The time is approaching when over two thirds of Asia the peoples will be left without a guiding star.

I missed the conclusion of the speech because of Igor. He and Fédor were sitting on either side of me on a little pile of straw, and how they did not set fire to it with their cigarettes was a mystery. Igor was asking me to marry him. As I did not answer (I was trying to follow what the speaker said), he pinched me behind. He wanted to know if we had enough money between us to get married on. When I said that I hadn't any, he sighed and said (in Chinese): 'Even the best of daughters-in-law cannot cook without rice!' I suppose this means that the bride should have some money, but the idea of my marrying Igor in order to cook rice for his parents set me off in a fit of the giggles. And this offended him very much. Igor is a beautiful boy, but I wish he would make love to Natasha. She would not mind his being a little 'wanting'. And I believe she is jealous of the attentions he pays to me.

When the speaker finished, he disappeared through

the door at the back of the hut. I did not see him again. But when we went out, there was a tall, slim Chinese with the peak of his cap lowered and the side of his face covered with ear-flaps. He was just starting down the hill, and the Russians all saluted him. I wonder if it was the same man.

To please Igor, I drank two or three little glasses of vodka. I am not used to strong drink, and when we started home in the icy evening air, I suddenly felt dizzy and had to sit down at the side of the path. No one noticed but Patushka, who was walking behind the others, with his head bent and looking homesick, as he always does when any one talks about Russia. He stared at me and asked if I were tired. I nodded. Then he took off his big fur coat and wrapped it round me, and he picked me up and carried me in his arms as easily as if I were a baby.

It was comfy, being carried like that, through the frozen fields. The others were far on ahead and we might have been all alone. Dogs barked in the villages. Stars sparkled in a frosty sky. My head and face were almost covered by the fur collar of Patushka's coat, but I caught a glimpse of the sky and saw the pointers and the Northern Star. As he walked, Patushka sang softly to himself.

When we reached the motor, he insisted that I should keep on his coat, and held me in his arms all the way home. He is rather a dear, poor old Patushka!

Twenty-ninth Day of the Eleventh Moon
The cold is terrible. Patushka says that five of the men that guard the railway line have been found this morning half frozen. Two of them have died. Thirty degrees of frost and a raging wind. It frightens me to hear it moaning round the corner tower of the Tartar Wall and over our roofs. Every now and then I hear a crash, as a loose tile falls on the stone flags of the courtyards.

King Cophetua went out very much wrapped up. He reappeared after a few minutes and asked if there were a bird-cage in the house. Pure Virtue keeps a bird and carries it about with him in its cage, covered round with blue cotton. But he and the bird had gone off to the market.

I asked King Cophetua why he wanted a cage, and he said there were some sparrows half frozen in the ditch opposite. They must have roosted somewhere on the Tartar Wall, probably in a hole where a brick was missing. But the wind had caught them there. We could not find a cage, so King Cophetua took a kettle, and I a teapot. We collected several sparrows and brought them home to recover in a warm room.

King Cophetua says we must put out trays of grain and seed, and hang lumps of suet on the trees, for the birds to eat. He prepared some lumps of suet himself, putting wire round them, so that the big birds should not carry them off whole, and sticking little wooden skewers into the suet, for the smaller birds to perch on while they eat.

Two of the sparrows have died (just like the men on the railway line). The others have recovered. I suggested letting them out again at the Gate of Happy Sparrows. It may bring them luck.

Uncle Podger took a great interest in the whole business and sniffed suspiciously at the kettle, while the sparrows were fluttering inside.

Thirtieth Day of the Eleventh Moon

No wind. A grey sky. Looks as if it might snow.

Went to see Sister Chiara at the convent. She tells me it is Christmas Eve. I had forgotten all about it. Since mother died I have never kept Christmas at home. But I remember she used to get a little fir-tree, and cover it with cotton-wool for snow, and shreds of silver paper for icicles. And she lit it up with coloured candles. It was very gay and pretty.

She called it a Christmas tree.

Seventh Day of the Twelfth Moon

My birthday.

The Five Virtues gave me a lot sweets and cakes, and they let off crackers in my honour. It was Little Lu's idea, and I hear that the Old Lady disapproved strongly. One should not celebrate the birthday of any one so young as I. Only after sixty is one really worthy. . . . King Cophetua asked Exalted Virtue what all the noise was about, and when he was told, he laughed and sent me his best wishes.

Matushka was sulky and irritable this morning, and she got worse as the day wore on. I had the ill-luck to annoy her twice during the afternoon, and the second time she took it out of me in the usual way.

I came home and went to my room and flung myself on the bed. I wanted to cry, and couldn't. I loathe that horrible birch! And on my birthday, too!

Then I noticed that the bed had an unaccustomed feeling, and I looked down to see what it could be. At my feet there was a goatskin rug, folded double, and underneath that a lovely fur coat of leopard skin. There was a card attached, one of King Cophetua's cards, and on it was written *Happy returns!* And then I burst into tears.

I think you have to be very young and alone in the world to know what kindness means.

But Uncle Podger is convinced that the goatskin rug is meant for him.

Twenty-ninth Day of the Twelfth Moon

End of the year. The old kitchen god has been burnt and his spirit – so the Old Lady says – has gone up to heaven to make report to 'the Pearly Emperor of All the Gods'! But the Five Virtues were careful to paste up his mouth with sticky toffee, so that he won't be able to tell how bad we have all been!

I think Uncle Podger must have eaten some of the toffee. He has been coughing and choking all the morning. Now he has been sick and feels better.

First Day of the First Moon

Chinese New Year. Everybody very festive. All debts paid. A new portrait of the kitchen god has been pasted up in the niche over the kitchen range, and we can start afresh.

I went to the convent and saw the Mother-Superior and Sister Chiara. They look so pretty in their coifs and white habits of nun's veiling. Sister Chiara says she has been having the usual difficulties of keeping those children out of class who are more obviously suffering from mumps or measles or small-pox. The parents seem to think that school is the best place for children when they're sick; better than home, anyway.

The nuns were very disapproving of my clothes. They said that my skirts were too short and my shoes wanted mending. Sister Chiara offered to come with me to the shops in the Hata Men, as soon as the New Year's festivities are over. She suggests buying some lengths of stuff for new frocks, and some Chinese cotton for underclothes. She says she can have them made for nothing to give practice to the native girls who are taught sewing in the convent.

In the days when I went to school and the nuns looked after me, I was always nicely dressed, with good shoes; my frocks were the proper length and I had plenty of fresh underclothes.

I wish I could go more often to see the nuns; in the old days they were like a family to me, and life was sheltered in the convent.

Outside, it is often like a desert dust-storm.

Second Day of the First Moon

When I went round to the Russian family this morning, Matushka was not visible and Patushka was looking very yellow. They had brought in the New Year with some friends at the Wu Tou Chü, a wine-shop near the execution ground. They must have eaten too many sharks' fins and drunk too much hot Shansi wine.

Patushka was about to start off on his annual visit to the Ch'iao Tung Pu, where his Chief is. But during the summer the moths, or the silver-fish, have eaten part of the rim of his top-hat. When the hat was brought out there was an awful row. We calmed him down and rallied to his help: Fédor with his paint-box (though what help that could be was not clear), and Natasha with needle and thread and a piece of black velvet from inside the hem of Matushka's only evening dress. While Natasha did her best with the hat, I emptied the naphthalene balls out of the pockets of Patushka's old frock-coat. In the end we got him off in a rickshaw. Fédor says that his father, with a top-hat on, looks like the leaning tower of Pisa. But I don't believe he was ever seen it.

After Patushka had left, Fédor wanted me to stay there with him. He had one of his amorous fits this morning. He gets them every now and then and becomes most vehement and tender. I never know what he is going to do next, and he does not mind who is present. He will make love to me in a room full of people. Natasha was there this morning and she said that if we were going to behave like that, she had better leave us. So she went off. After which Fédor asked me to let him do some sketches of my knees. He says knees are very difficult to draw properly. As a matter of fact, he wanted rather more than my knees, but he stopped making love to me as soon as he had a sketch-book and a pencil in his hand. He would have kept me there all the morning, but the number one boy came in with a message from Matushka: she wanted Fédor to get her some bismuth cachets from the German chemist in the Hata Men.

So I put on my stockings and came home.

Third Day of the First Moon

King Cophetua never can understand how it is that, during the festivities for the New Year, the Chinese in Peking all go to visit the houses in the Quarter of the Eight Big Hutungs, and take their families with them. I always wanted to go there as a child, because the Five Virtues used to take Little Lu, and not me. They did not want to take me to-day. So perhaps Chinese girls are not taken as a rule; only boys. But as a foreign girl I can do what I please, and I insisted on going too. We visited two houses in Willow Street Lane. I found them very dull. The first place we went to was called 'The Garden of Kingfisher Coloured Fairies'. But the fairies were fat and more like quails than kingfishers. The last fashion is for them to wear motor-caps of foreign pattern, which looks odd with jade ear-rings and brocade coats. Everybody drank tea and smoked cigarettes, and it was all very formal and respectable.

Afterwards we went to the fair of the Liu-li-chang, where we met King Cophetua buying snuff-bottles. He greeted the Five Virtues very affably and took Little Lu and me to see some dolls dancing on a big brass plate that is beaten with a wooden hammer to make it vibrate. King Cophetua gave us each a fly-whisk, very brightly coloured, to chase away the evil spirits.

Though I had on my new leopard-skin coat, I felt very cold standing about in the courtyards of the Liu-li-chang. I wish I could wear long trousers, like the Peking girls. If I were dressed Chinese fashion and showed less of my legs, perhaps Fédor might not be so enterprising.

Sixth Day of the First Moon

Patushka and Matushka were out when I went round this morning. And Fédor was painting a portrait-head of Natasha in oils, on the panel of the schoolroom door. I told him that he would get into trouble when his parents came home. But he said that he had no canvases left and that the room would look much better with the doors all painted by him. On the panel, opposite Natasha, he meant to paint Igor.

As they were all busy, I came away. I didn't want to get mixed up in the row when Patushka and Matushka turned up.

Seventh Day of the First Moon

I was right about what would happen when Patushka and Matushka came home and found the painting on the door panel. To-day Fédor is very sore and down in the mouth.

But still he can think of nothing but his painting. He complains that he cannot get any models. There are no white models in Peking. The only foreigner who will pose for him is Igor. Some of the Chinese men are all right, but the girls are no use. They won't undress.

Natasha is not much good as a model; her figure is rotten, though it may improve as she grows older.

Fédor wants me to pose for him, and I would rather not. I don't know what Papà would say about it, and I'm certain that King Cophetua would disapprove strongly if he knew. Fédor and I had a long argument about it again this morning. Although he is not so big and strong as his father, I generally get the worst of arguments with Fédor. His parents make no attempt to keep him in order, as far as I am concerned, though they are always ready to whip him, poor boy, if he annoys *them!*

I don't know how the argument about posing for him will end. Natasha jeers at me for refusing, and I'm sure his parents would think it all right. It is a pity that he cannot be content with painting Igor. This afternoon, while Natasha and I were writing at the schoolroom table, Igor stood near the piano, stark naked, while Fédor did some sketches of him in an album, and complained that there was not enough light. Fédor says that Igor looks like Cupid and ought to have wings.

Tenth Day of the First Moon

Part of Patushka's religious feeling – so he says – can only be expressed by dancing. And now he has got it into his head that he will teach Natasha and me some Russian dances, to make us graceful. He is not very graceful himself; he is too big. But he might teach quite well, if he could keep his mind on what he is doing. While showing us the steps, he picks us up and puts us down, as though we were no heavier than his violin. You would think he was playing with dolls. And sometimes he will leave us in the middle of a lesson and go off on his own affairs, forgetting all about us, like a child that leaves its doll on the floor, because it has thought of something more amusing.

The lessons started with a great deal of flourish. Fédor designed some 'working' costumes for us: black tunics, open at the side, and cream-coloured silk knickers. Very saucy indeed! On the first day there were three Russian girls, besides Natasha and me. To-day we had a lesson and only one Russian girl turned up. As the costumes are not ready (and I do not suppose they ever will be!), we take off our frocks and wear little woollen sweaters above our pants. Which reminds me: the next time I get some money from Papà, I must go with Sister Chiara to the Clock Store and get some stuff for new pants. I have nothing left but some skimpy little drawers that I've had for years and am always bursting out of!

Twelfth Day of the First Moon

Fédor asked me to-day if I wasn't in love with Igor. When I said No, he seemed disappointed. Yet he had been kissing me himself a moment before.

'Why should I be in love with Igor?' I asked. 'He is a perfect fool. I always feel that he's never going to grow up.'

'Yes. He's like Parsifal. But you might have fallen in love with him all the same.'

'Do you want me to?'

'No. I would rather you fell in love with me. As a matter of fact, you will probably end by marrying your King Cophetua. Now if it had been Igor, I might have persuaded you to pose with him. You would make a lovely group as Psyche and Eros.'

He shook his head dolefully, sighed, kissed me again, and went off into the town to get some drawing-paper.

107

It is not easy to follow what Fédor has in his mind. But it all comes down to his painting in the end. I wonder what made him say that about King Cophetua?

Fifteenth Day of the First Moon

To-day is the Feast of the Lanterns, and the Five Virtues were busy making *yuan hsiaos*, little white balls of sugar and barley flour with red jelly inside. I offered one to Uncle Podger, who sniffed at it contemptuously and yawned. But he accepted a meat dumpling instead.

Matushka also was in the kitchen, cooking *borsch* with *schi*, a wonderful broth of meat and cabbages, and a dish called *kasha*, which should be made with the finest millet. But she had to make shift with Chinese *kao-liang*. There was a smell of cabbages all over the house.

We had another dancing lesson from Patushka, but only Natasha and I were there. All the Russian girls have dropped out. Fédor suggests that we should take on Igor and turn him into a new Nijinsky. I dare say it wouldn't be a bad idea.

Natasha does not care for this kind of dancing. She is a bit on the lumpy side and is stupid and sulky about it. Then Patushka gets annoyed with both of us, though I am quite willing to do my best. To-day, Matushka left her cooking to play the piano for us. But Natasha muddled the steps and confused me. After several attempts to get it right, both Patushka and Matushka lost their tempers. It ended by Natasha and I flying for our lives!

We got away just in time.

There is a big wind, and it looks as if it might get worse. When there is a 'yellow wind' in Peking, people's tempers get a bit frayed.

Sixteenth Day of the First Moon

They call the date *Yu shuè*, 'rain water', but I never heard of it raining in Peking at this season. At the most there may be a little water in the rain-tub, which up till now has been frozen too solid to use.

108

This is the third day of wind and dust. Everybody as cross as two sticks. Even King Cophetua is irritable and ousted the Old Lady from the guest-room, where she was poking her nose for no reason that she could explain.

Uncle Podger's tail is blown right and left as he crosses the courtyards. But he does not lose his dignity.

The Russian family are all so nervy as to be almost dangerous. Only Igor moons about the house and beams, good-naturedly as usual.

I hope this wind will go down in the night.

Seventeenth Day of the First Moon

Wind worse than ever. The garden covered with yellow sand from the desert. I watched the coolies going round the outer pavilions, muffled up to the ears and carrying paste-pots and rice paper, to repair the damage done to the windows. I can write my name in the dust on the furniture, and whenever I touch metal I get an electric shock. I even got one by dipping my finger into the bowl of water on top of the stove, to see if it were hot.

When the rickshaw coolie put me down at the Russian family's house, their number one boy opened the door only a little and stuck his head out. There was a large cross of plaster on his forehead.

'Missee more better go 'way *kwi-kwi*,' he said.

'What's happened to your head?' I asked. 'Did some one throw a plate at you?'

'No plate. Teapot. And Missee Natasha catchee plenty. . . .'

Just then we heard Matushka calling. And the boy shut the door hurriedly, leaving me outside.

I made a sign to the rickshaw coolie, and he took me home *kwi-kwi* (quick-quick) as suggested.

When I got home, Exalted Virtue said that the Great Man had something to say to me, so I went to King Cophetua's study. I found him with Mr. Tang, having a Chinese lesson. When he saw me he said:

'There is an announcement in the paper that the

Peking Pavilion is giving an Italian film, a screen version of the *Promessi Sposi*. You know so little of your own country that you ought to see it. I will take you to-morrow evening, if you care to go.'

I accepted with enthusiasm and was going out of the room again, when King Cophetua asked me: 'How is it that you are not with the Russian family?'

'When I got to their door, the Chinese boy advised me to go away. There was trouble inside.'

King Cophetua turned to Mr. Tang and said:

'It seems to be the rule in China, when there is trouble anywhere, to keep well away. Is that one of the maxims of Confucius?'

Mr. Tang took the question quite seriously. He thought it over and then told us a story:

'The Master taught us that it is best to take our troubles as they come and where they come. And this is how He Himself learnt that lesson. He was travelling with His disciples, when He came upon a woman weeping beside a newly made tomb. He asked her:

' "For whom do you mourn?"

'And she answered: "For my son."

'The Master looked round and beheld other tombs. And He asked who was buried there. The woman answered:

' "My husband and my daughter."

' "And how did they die?"

' "They also were killed by a tiger."

' "If the tigers are so dangerous in these parts, why don't you go away and live elsewhere?"

'And the woman answered:

' "The Government does not trouble us much, just here." '

Eighteenth Day of the First Moon

King Cophetua took me to see the film of the *Promessi Sposi*. There were some Chinese in the box next to us, who seemed to think that the arrival of the *Landsknechte* in Lombardy and the scenes of the plague in Milan were taken from the war on the Italian front.

Though he is kindness itself, King Cophetua does not often take notice of me, and this is the first time he has asked me to go out with him anywhere. I think that he really wanted to ask me some questions about what he calls my 'finishing course in a bear garden'.

I wish I could tell him about it. I want some one to confide in, and it would be nice to take my troubles to him as I did when I was a child and fell down and grazed my knees. Then he would take me on his knee and pet me and give me chocolates. I'm afraid that, if I told him my troubles now, he would merely write to Papà. And Papà has worries enough of his own, with Chinese generals fighting all over his railway line.

So whatever happens, I have to tell King Cophetua that it is all right and rather funny, whereas he is convinced that if, after frequenting the Russian family for a year or two, I am still a *kuniang*, it will be more by good luck than good management. I sometimes wonder if he may not be right, for Fédor is inclined to be difficult. He is so strong and primitive in the midst of all these Chinese! What he says and does goes to my head like wine. It is not that I'm in love with him, but on the whole it is lucky that he thinks more of his art than of me.

Nineteenth Day of the First Moon

The Russian family were even crazier than usual to-day.

The wind had gone down and they were all in the best of tempers, but dazed, as they always are after a dust-storm.

Patushka won't give dancing lessons to Natasha any more (and she does not want them!). This morning he said that I might have a lesson all to myself. So I ran and took off my frock.

But after he had played a Cossack dance on his violin, Patushka forgot all about me. He sat on the sofa singing, with his chin cupped in his hands, and he kept staring in front of him as if, beyond the schoolroom walls, he saw

the fields and the woods of his old home. I could understand a few words of his song, which was about a fruit-
ful soil that was not furrowed by the plough, but by the
hoofs of horses, and white fish that leapt above the
waters of the River Don. There does not seem to be anything very sad in this, and yet Patushka's eyes filled with
tears, and there were tears in my eyes too.

And the stove had gone out. The room was very cold. I
stood shivering with my hands in the pockets of my little
sweater, trying to pull it down. My skin was all goose-
fleshy above my stockings. I sneezed, and this brought
me a glance from Patushka, but he took no further notice.
To keep myself warm, I started doing exercises, swaying
round from the waist and bending down to touch the
floor. But my poor old pants could not stand the strain,
and I felt the buttons go off with a *ping!*

On the schoolroom table there is an old cup with the
handle missing and full of pen-nibs and bits of sealing-
wax, and occasionally a safety-pin. I searched for something to pin myself up with, but the safety-pins were no
longer there.

Just then Fédor came into the room and began to
unroll a sheet of drawing-paper that was lying among
the music scores on the piano. He seemed busy and paid
no attention to me. Patushka left the sofa and put his
violin away in its case. It was clear that he had given up
all thought of a dancing lesson. But he glanced at me
with a puzzled expression. Evidently he felt that he must
have forgotten something that he had to do about me and
wondered why I was standing there with my pants held
up precariously with one hand.

'Are you waiting there for Matushka to come and give
you a whipping?' he asked. 'Or ought *I* to be seeing
about it?'

I was so taken aback that I could only gape at him,
though at the mere mention of a whipping my face began
to burn. Patushka took this for assent, but he had
qualms. He shook his head and remarked:

'I really could not use a birch on a little slip of a thing like you. Come here and I'll spank you.'

He was quite kind and gentle about it, but I was utterly tongue-tied, and would have taken what was coming if Fédor had not interposed. He did so only just in time.

'You know, little father,' he said, 'it's not that at all.'

'Not that? What do you mean?'

'Kuniang was getting ready to pose for me.'

Patushka is not quick in the uptake. He thought the matter over before he decided that it must be as Fédor had said. Then he set me on my feet again and smiled.

'Certainly, you could find no better model for a young girl. But you must not let poor Kuniang pose in here. It is much too cold. I'll tell you what! You can use the guest-room as a studio. Have the stove lit, and when it is warm take her up there.'

He patted me on the head and strolled off, humming the 'Volga Boatmen'. A minute later I heard him calling for his rickshaw to take him to the office. How Patushka manages to keep his job at that office is more than I can tell.

Fédor chuckled delightedly.

'I saved you there, Kuniang!' he said. 'And now you cannot refuse to pose for me. I will have the stove lit upstairs.'

'Fédor! You know I don't want to.'

He came closer and took me in his arms.

'What *do* you want, little dove?' he asked. 'Do you want to be loved? If you won't let me paint you, I will certainly make love to you. Choose: one or the other, since you don't want both.'

'And what if I let you paint me, and I were alone with you, all naked? Would you be content with a few kisses?'

'Little dove, did I ever bother you when we bathed together in the swimming-pool? Or when we had sun-baths afterwards, lying on the grass in the garden? Yet then you were quite bare. I used to watch you and make sketches afterwards, from memory, of your loveliness. I am an artist, and though I can feel the torment of desire, it is not when I have a palette on my thumb and a canvas before me, with the colours all there to my hand. Then I feel only the passion to create. Pose for me, Kuniang, and I'll promise to be good.'

I said I would think it over.

But I see how it will end.

Third Day of the Second Moon

I suppose that Confucius was right and that it is best to take one's troubles as they come and where they come!

Not that I have been in trouble exactly, but I posed for the first time, as Fédor wanted me. He was very pleased and even contrived what he calls 'a model's throne', a sort of raised platform on which I sit or stand. We used the guest-room, and it was quite warm with the stove lit. It is the best bedroom in the house, though rarely used as such. They keep all sorts of queer Russian groceries in there, and smoked fish, and ikons, and Chinese curios.

It was one of the curios that embarrassed me most while I posed. I think I will ask to have it taken away. There is a Laughing Buddha on the mantelpiece; one of those porcelain figures of Milo Fo, with a large bare tummy and unctuous smile. When I first stepped up on to the model's throne, I met the Buddha's eye and I gasped. Fédor noticed this and chuckled:

'A leering old devil, isn't he, Kuniang? Not like me. I can look you over with the eye of an artist. Now I'm sure King Cophetua would lose his head completely if he saw you as you are now.'

I could not help smiling. 'I dare say you are right,' I said. 'Anyhow, I had better not tell him, or I must break it to him gently. Otherwise he would be horribly shocked.'

Fédor gave a snort of contempt.

'I have no patience,' he said, 'with people who are shocked about posing in the altogether. The human body in its perfection is used to represent everything spiritual. We take a tender maiden, and she impersonates the immortal soul. We take a beautiful youth, and he is the sun god, many-sided as men are, and with the foresight that is divine. I wonder sometimes if the man's figure is not the more perfect, especially when almost feminine in its fulness. But when I see you naked, I know that the sheer ecstasy of a young virgin's beauty has no parallel among men.'

I never knew that Fédor felt like that, or could talk like that about my figure, or anything!

But the Laughing Buddha on the mantelpiece smiled his leering, oily smile.

Eighteenth Day of the Second Moon
To-day is what the Chinese calendar calls *Ching Ch'è*, 'Excited Insects'. I saw a line of rickshaw coolies sitting with their backs to a sun-baked wall and going over their clothes. Possibly the insects were a bit *too* excited.

I thought perhaps that the bug which I found in my room one day last autumn, and failed to catch, might have joined in the general excitement. But he made no sign. I suppose Exalted Virtue really did do something about it, as he said he had (though he accused me of having brought the bug from the Russian family's house!).

I believe to-day's date is really important to farmers in the country. Something to do with the insects waking up to fertilize the flowers. But such things mean little to town-dwellers, who live in the shadow of the Tartar Wall. Even the Happy Sparrows at our stable door seem to say:

'We do not depend for our food on crops or berries. Ours are the pickings of the Forbidden City!'

115

8 'The Incandescent Lily'

There is a novel by Gouverneur Morris that bears this title. It tells about an American youth, who is engaged to a lovely young heiress and nevertheless goes off into the interior of China in search of rare flowers and bulbs for the Boston Arboretum. He reaches the edge of a valley into which he cannot penetrate, because the way on every side is barred by a precipice. But one night, while he sleeps, he is chloroformed and carried off by the emissaries of a Chinese princess, who rules in that valley, and he is taken by hidden paths to her palace. The pride of her kingdom is a sacred lily with phosphorescent petals, which the priests of the temple cherish as the holy of holies. Naturally the young botanist wants to take some bulbs home. And naturally he may not do so. The princess falls in love with him and wants him to stay with her for ever. But in the end he is chloroformed once more and taken out of the valley, bulbs and all. And the princess gets left. It is a fantastic little story, delightfully told.

There are plenty of young botanists who disappear into the almost unexplored regions of south-western China in search of specimens and bulbs. They reappear after some time, bringing with them natural trophies and even more wonderful travellers' tales, though I never heard that any of them found an incandescent lily, or a *princesse lointaine*.

But Gouverneur Morris's novel is connected in my mind with a journey in China, accomplished by Lord Randolph Seymor, a young aristocrat who had acquired a reputation for eccentricity owing to his mania for disappearing for long periods in search of rare botanical specimens. A similar mania, in so very eligible a young man, did not appeal to the mammas of society débutantes. And not a few of the girls themselves doubtless thought that, if he must travel in search of flowers, he might take one of them along on a honeymoon.

Meanwhile Lord Randolph brought back from Brazil a new orchid, to which he gave his name, and which is now one of the glories of the hot-houses in Kew Gardens. What is perhaps more to the point, his hobby brought him in a considerable income. The search for new specimens, especially of unknown varieties of common flowers, can be very remunerative.

In the spring of 1914 Lord Randolph started off to explore the valleys north-west of Yunnan. He was seeking primulas, which in that part of the world abound in varieties unknown in the West. When he passed through Peking I mentioned to him the novel by Gouverneur Morris and made him promise that, should he ever find an incandescent lily, he would let me have a bulb or two for my garden.

Lord Randolph travelled up the Yangtze gorges to Chunking, whence he disappeared along the road to Kweichow and was not heard of again till February 1916, when he emerged at Canton, coming down the Blue River. His reappearance in western circles caused a certain amount of amusement, because he was quite unconscious that a world war was in progress. Nor did the fact appear to interest him. Like many other people, he did not realize at once the extent of the conflagration, and was annoyed only because of the difficulties in sending home his specimens. The officials of the British Legation provoked his outspoken disapproval because they refused to let him send his bulbs to London in the diplomatic 'bag'.

He returned to Peking in April, almost two years after he had started for the interior, and established himself temporarily in a Chinese house, near the Hata Men, while he prepared an account of his journey with the intention of publishing it when he reached England again.

The furnishing of his house was typical of the Far East, where two civilizations meet. Together with modern office furniture were Shansi cupboards in red lacquer and large hardwood chairs. Spread about on the tables and on top of the cupboards were Chinese curios and American canned goods; snuff-bottles of jade and agate, bottles of gin and vermuth, boxes of cigars and vases of K'ang-hsi porcelain. A bronze Buddha studied the reflection of his own smile in the cover of a portable typewriter. Brocades of green and gold hung on the walls, and pinned on to them were maps, showing the itinerary of Lord Randolph's journeys. A Kodak, a pair of guns, a mandarin's hat complete with peacock's feathers, a camp bed, and a collection of seals were also included in the inventory.

Lord Randolph and I used to meet often at his house or mine. He had a pleasant way of telling his experiences, though some of his stories were meant to be taken with a grain of salt. One of these concerned a religious ceremony instituted, at his own suggestion, in a monastery on the confines of Tibet, in the territory of the Charchund tribe. Every evening, in the most secluded hall of the monastery, Lord Randolph and the abbot would prepare a stimulating beverage, which had to be shaken for some time in a metal gourd, together with small pieces of ice. The ingredients had been brought thus far by Lord Randolph himself, and he would share the resulting nectar with no one of lesser rank than the abbot, who gave him many facilities in exchange for such a signal favour.

Some of Lord Randolph's descriptions of the country he had travelled over made me want to start botanizing myself. He spoke of a green valley, sloping down between snow-covered peaks. On either side of a foaming torrent were meadows covered with tiny violet-hued blossoms (*Callistephus sinensis*), and, above these, long-stalked poppies swayed in the breeze, producing marvellous effects of changing colours.

One evening in May, Lord Randolph and I dined together on the terrace of the Peking Club. He was talking as usual about his researches among the Chinese flora, when I suddenly remembered what I had said to him before he started on his journey inland. And I asked him jestingly if he had ever come across an incandescent lily. Rather to my surprise, he did not answer at once. Finally he said:

'I never found the lily or the princess, at least, not as described in the story you told me, but I had an adventure which reminded me, I don't know why, of what you said.'

'What happened?'

Lord Randolph looked round as if to make sure that no one would hear. A party of Russians were partaking of zakouska a little farther down the terrace, but there were no other diners near our table. So while we drank our coffee he told me the following story:

'At the end of my tour in Yunnan, I came down the Blue River by boat, passing through the silk district. We tied up for the night at a bend of the river, in the lee of a small promontory that jutted out into the stream. On the farther side of the river the plain began, but on the nearer side the banks were broken and precipitous. Close to the promontory, about twenty yards downstream, a detached mass of rock formed a tiny islet, on which there rose a miniature temple, with a single pavilion, from which a flight of steps led down to the water's edge. Its columns, lacquered in red, its uptilted angles and an ornamental balustrade which was falling into ruins, brought a note of the minute and the artificial into the vast natural panorama.

'Inside the temple was the usual effigy of the Buddha, and a row of sacrificial vases on an oblong table: outside

119

the usual incense burner and a bell, hanging from a heavy wooden frame. This was the Temple of the Incandescent Lily.'

'But why . . .?'

'Wait and I will tell you. My two boats were moored about three hundred yards downstream from the islet. A mile off was the village where my *lowdah* went to procure provisions. I stayed on board till late, tending my bulbs. Only after supper did I step on shore, to take a stroll in the moonlight. I might not have done so, but I was bothered by the attentions of a leper, one of those unfortunates who paddle about on the river and never seem to land anywhere. They use canoes that are painted white so as to be recognizable from far off, and they beg from the passing junks and from the mat-shed houses along the river banks, tendering a small bag at the end of a long stick of bamboo. People throw the remains of their meals into the bag, and occasionally a copper coin. In this way they can be charitable without risk of contact and infection. The leper that came round our boats after dusk had no face left. He looked like some obscene spirit floating on the surface of the water. Although I had thrown him the remains of my own supper and a silver dollar, he would not go away. To get rid of him, I went on shore and started walking along the towpath in the direction of the promontory and the islet. It must have been about nine o'clock. In the moonlight the islet with its little temple looked utterly unreal.

'When I stopped for a moment to gaze on the scene, which was like a piece of stage scenery, a woman came out of the temple and walked slowly down the steps to the water's edge. And there she remained, silent, but with her arms held out towards me. The light of the moon was so strong that I could see every detail of her clothes and figure. She wore a pair of silk trousers, bound in at the ankle, and that's all.'

'Rather unusual in this country.'

'Very. So much so that at first I doubted her being

Chinese at all. Her skin was much whiter than that of the river people. And she was pretty in a doll-like way. I imagined her to be some local *yao-ch'er*, who had chosen those unusual surroundings for a background to her charms.

'The night was warm. I swam out, like Lord Byron to the house of his mistress in Venice. And that was my adventure. The strange part of it all is that, after coming away again, at midnight, I never saw the lady again. I told her to wait for me while I brought her some money (I had none with me), and she said she would, but when I went back she was not there, and though we waited till the next evening before starting south, she did not make an appearance. That is why I think she must have been a princess, for *yao-ch'ers* do not offer their favours for nothing, in China or elsewhere.'

'Did you make any inquiries in the vicinity?'

'I told the *lowdah* to do so, but he assured me he could discover nothing. And he warned me not to have anything to do with the woman, saying that she must be a water-ghost and would drown me, or a spirit-fox and would suck my blood like a vampire.'

'Those are common ideas in China. I suppose that, in the daytime, the woman would take the shape of a big fish or a fox. But still I do not see why you called her the Incandescent Lily.'

'Because of the singular whiteness of her skin, which had something almost luminous about it. I wonder if she were not a half-caste, from Canton or from Macao. But even that does not explain why she should have shown herself so disinterested in her dealing with a stranger.'

'Were her feet artificially deformed?'

'No. But that would not mean anything. Many of the women among the poorer classes along the river have natural feet.'

'And are you sure you did not dream it all from start to finish?'

'I thought of that too. . . . The whole thing is like a

story by Pierre Loti. But next day, when I visited the little temple once more, I found a faded flower on the ground, a spray of yellow jasmine, and I remembered that she had worn it in her hair.'

Before we separated after dinner that night at the Club, Lord Randolph and I decided to go off on an excursion together, to visit various places of interest in the Western Hills; one of the usual picnics that every one takes from Peking, travelling partly on foot and partly in chairs or on donkeys. It was not the temples that interested Lord Randolph. He said he was sick of temples. But I happened to mention that I had found edelweiss on the hills at the back of the Chieh T'ai Ssè, and that gave him the idea that the flora of the hills near Peking might not be unworthy of his notice.

I don't know how Lord Randolph managed during his journeys into the interior, but I found him singularly lacking in moderation when it came to distributing largess among the priests in the temples and the children and beggars in the villages. More than once we were mobbed by the enthusiastic recipients of his bounty, and on one occasion I had to use my stick freely in order to force my way out of a crowd that pressed around the imprudently generous foreign devil.

'I suppose,' I said huffily, when Lord Randolph rejoined me, 'that you think it is your duty to distribute in China the money that you make here by collecting herbaceous perennials. But I wish you would do so when I am not with you.'

Lord Randolph laughed and dusted his jacket, which his admirers had been pawing with dirty hands. He suggested that, if we climbed the nearest hill, we might get a good view of the valley of Men-to-kou, and while enjoying it, consume the sandwiches and empty the flasks that we had brought with us.

The sanctuary where we had decided to pass the night was the one known as the Temple of the White Pines. Our servants had gone ahead to prepare for our coming. As we had not much farther to go, we took it easy. Lord Randolph poked about, picking up small flowers and gazing at them through a pocket lens. I enjoyed the breeze, the view and the pure hill air, and thought to myself that I must really rent a temple somewhere near, and come and live in it occasionally, as so many foreigners do.

It was almost dark when we made our way down the hill-side, and perhaps because he could not see where he placed his feet, Lord Randolph suddenly slipped and rolled down the steep incline amid a clutter of small stones.

I called out: 'Have you hurt yourself?', but he did not answer. However, when I joined him again, he was standing up looking himself over. The only damage apparent was a tear in his nether garments and several scratches in his hands.

We got home – so to speak – a little before eight, and found Exalted Virtue and Lord Randolph's own boy lighting the kerosene lamps that they had brought with them.

A few minutes later, Lord Randolph, seated on the side of his camp bed, contemplated the tear in his beautifully made plus-fours.

'That's odd,' he said. 'I must have cut my leg.'

A little below the calf of his right leg, a small trickle of blood had reddened the stocking. He pulled it down, and there, embedded, in the flesh was a long, sharp thorn. It was easy to pull out, and fortunately I had with me an 'iodine pencil'. I went to fetch it from my suit-case.

When I returned, Lord Randolph was still sitting at the side of the bed.

'It is very odd,' he said, 'that I should feel no pain.'

The fact that he felt no pain seemed something to be thankful for, but in his voice there was a tone of anxiety. He looked uneasy.

I examined the wound. It was by no means a serious one, but certainly it was curious that it should not be painful.

'And if you touch it,' I asked, 'do you feel any discomfort?'

Lord Randolph began to press with his fingers up and down the calf of his leg. 'Here I do,' he said; 'here I feel nothing. It is almost as if I had been given an injection of cocaine. There could hardly be a drug on that thorn. I wonder if it is merely a symptom of fatigue?'

For a few moments, I remained standing beside him, wondering what could be the reason for that strange insensibility. And then the explanation – the *possible* explanation – flashed through my mind. I went out of the room, so that Lord Randolph should not guess from my face the feeling of nausea that had suddenly come over me.

It was the memory of a story I had once read, that gave me a clue: the story of Father Damien, who organized the colony of lepers at Molokai, and how he first discovered that he himself had contracted the fatal disease. Returning from a search for a spring that should furnish his camp with fresh water, he pulled off his boots and found that his feet were blistered and bleeding, *but he felt no pain*. That was the first sign of the *lepra anestetica*, due to the granulation on a nerve, destroying sensibility.

I had gone out into the courtyard and was standing there, uncertain what to do and what to say to my companion, when I heard a step behind me and a hand was laid on my shoulder. Lord Randolph had followed me. Although he was so close, it was too dark for me to see his face.

'What do you think?' he asked. 'Can it be the symptom of a – serious illness?'

'I don't think so,' I answered, trying to make my voice sound reassuring. 'More likely it is a local insensibility, due to the general stiffness of fatigue.'

Lord Randolph sighed and went indoors again. I followed him and we sat down opposite one another at a rickety table, where our boys had set out supper. A plate stood near Lord Randolph, with a long-shaped loaf on it. He cut a few slices and held out the plate for me to take one. I did so, and in that simple act betrayed my fears, for I chose the slice that his hand had not touched. He noticed it and said quietly:

'You are right. We must be careful. I will tell the boy to keep my glass and knife and fork apart from yours.'

What could I say? I did not answer, and we continued our supper in silence. When we had finished, we went out and sat on the few steps that led from the central pavilion down into the courtyard. Bars of light from the lamps inside lay on the stone flags and wavered as the boys moved about inside the rooms, preparing our camp-beds and putting up the mosquito curtains.

'How do you think I can have caught it?' asked Lord Randolph.

Neither of us had yet pronounced the word 'leprosy', but it was useless to pretend not to understand. I felt sure that he expected me to confirm his own suspicions. After a moment's hesitation, I answered:

'From the Incandescent Lily.'

'But why?'

I thought it best, as he showed so much courage, to tell him what I had in my mind.

'It is a superstition,' I said, 'among Chinese of the southern provinces, that you can cure yourself of that illness by passing it on to others in a love-embrace.'

Lord Randolph did not say anything. He got up and began to walk up and down. For many hours after I had gone to bed and lay under the mosquito net, unable to sleep, I heard him still pacing up and down the stone flags in the courtyard.

Next morning we returned to Peking, and for a few days I did not meet him or hear of him. I did not like to go and see him myself, to find out if my suspicions were correct. Sooner or later he would let me know. And then, one morning, I met Charlie Lyons, of the British Legation, who asked me:

'Have you heard about Lord Randolph?'

'Heard what?'

'He has suddenly discovered that there is a war on in Europe and he wants to start for the front at a moment's notice. He would even pay for a special train, supposing that to be feasible. But as it is not, he passes his time sending telegrams to people in England, asking them to push the matter through at once, so that he should not have to go in for any preliminary training at home. He is willing to go as cook or chaplain, but go he must. And he talks as if he expected to lead a charge of the Light Brigade the morning he arrives. I can't make out what's got the man!'

'Do you think he will put it through?'

'Sure to. He is related to half the House of Lords. His brother is at the War Office, and an uncle is colonel of a regiment somewhere on the Somme. Also his sister is married to a Cabinet Minister, who hates Randolph like poison. He will do his best to put him in "the forefront of the battle". But the funny part of it all is that till a few days ago he never said a word about wanting to join the Army. All he talked about was primroses.'

That same evening, Lord Randolph came to see me, bringing a large sheaf of papers in a leather case.

'It is the MS. of my book of travels,' he explained, 'with all the data of my botanical researches. I want to leave it in your hands, so that it may be published when the war is over. Somebody at Kew Gardens might look over the proofs, to see that there are no mistakes in the part about the flowers and bulbs.'

'Why not send it straight to your publisher?'

'Too risky, in these times of stress. And I dare not take it with me. Travelling is difficult enough just now without carrying papers with you. People want to examine them at every frontier. I am leaving you a written authorization to dedicate the proceeds to some charity in the Far East. Between ourselves I would like you to send them to the Franciscan Sisters in Mandalay.'

126

'Why Mandalay?'

'It is the mission that cares for the lepers.'

'You may be sure that I will do as you wish. When do you leave Peking?'

'Next Wednesday, by the Trans-Siberian to St. Petersburg, and then by Sweden and Bergen to Hull or Newcastle. Everything is arranged for me to go straight to France, to join my uncle's regiment. I need only stop in London a few hours to get the uniform that my tailors will have ready?'

'But are you sure that . . .?'

'Quite sure. I can just get back in time for nobody to know.'

'And then?'

'I am told that it is dangerous to look over the top of the trenches. But anyway, I will arrange to figure among the dead or missing. At the worst, I will tell my uncle and ask him to help me to a soldier's death, without dragging others into danger.'

'Why not try to get well? I believe it is not impossible, if taken in time.'

'So the doctor here tells me. He speaks of "arrested cases." But I must live decently, or not at all. I think most people would agree with me in preferring to figure in a list of casualties. . . . But there is no time to lose.'

He remained with me a little longer, speaking about the MS. of his book. When he got up to leave, he held out his hand to say good-bye. During the whole of his call he had not taken off his gloves.

The name of Lord Randolph Seymor was published in the *Roll of Honour* in July 1916. He died during the offensive, north of the Somme, on the plateau of Pozières. *Felix opportunitate mortis*. . . .

He must have spoken or written about me to his sister, for I received a letter from her full of kind expressions of gratitude and sympathy for 'poor Randolph's friend'. Later, she sent me a photograph of the coloured glass window, set up to his memory in the family chapel.

He appears therein, in the character of St. George. Under the figure there is a verse from the Bible, but the lettering was too small for me to read in the photograph. I imagine that the quotation is *not* taken from the fifth chapter in the Second Book of Kings, where it speaks of Naaman: 'For he was a rich man, and great in valour . . . but a leper!'

9   The Dogs of Lu-Tai

Something Kuniang said about the dogs that congregate round the gates of Peking (where there are eating-houses for people arriving from the country) reminded me of the dogs of Lu-tai.

The station of Lu-tai is situated at the northern extremity of the marshy plain, which stretches along the sea-coast, near the mouth of the Hai Ho. I mention the station, because I know nothing of Lu-tai except the station platform, nor have I any desire to extend my knowledge of the locality. The Peking-Mukden express, northward bound, stops there on the double line, about two p.m., and waits for the corresponding train to pass southward. According to the time-table, one should not stop at Lu-tai for more than five minutes, but it often happens that one has to wait for half an hour or more.

On getting out of the train, to walk up and down the platform, one is struck by the wretched appearance of the dogs and of the beggars, who come to the station at the hour when the train passes. One first notices the dogs, because they may come close up to the train, whereas the beggars are kept at a distance by a picket of Chinese soldiers, who pace the platform, armed with rifle and bayonet, and do not allow the mendicant community to approach. The beggars have to stand on the farther side of a wooden paling, where they make pitiful gestures of appeal and call out in raucous voices: 'Ta Laiè! (Great man! Great man!).' Most of the beggars behind the paling are old women. In those shapeless masses of rags, the sex is recognizable by the small, artificially deformed feet. The 'lily feet' that an Empress brought into fashion are to-day a sign of the eternal feminine in the poor hungry wretches behind a paling at Lu-tai.

Even the dogs, who vie with the old women in the struggle for life, appear to have fallen to the lowest depth of the canine social scale. They inspire more disgust than compassion. Pitifully thin, generally lame, covered with sores and vermin, they wander in and out among the wheels of the railway cars, sniffing the ground in the hopes of finding some scrap of food that has been thrown out of the carriage windows.

And here we may point out a characteristic that the dogs of Lu-tai share with those of the rest of China: they never lift their heads to meet the glance of the travellers and to ask them, with whines and tail-wagging, for a scrap for food. They keep their eyes on the ground, waiting for something to fall, and when it does, they seize it and gulp it down in haste, lest the person who dropped it should wish to pick it up again. Accustomed as they have been, through endless generations, never to receive anything from man, they place no hopes in his generosity, but only in his carelessness. Kuniang has a tender heart, especially where animals are concerned, and it was she who first brought this trait in Chinese *wonks* (as they are called) to my notice. But the fact is typical of more than the Oriental attitude towards stray dogs. It reflects the pessimism that lies at the heart of an otherwise jovial and patient people. Charity on a small scale to dogs or men (except to professional beggars, who levy a kind of blackmail) is futile in a country of such teeming millions. It only brings round more and more supplicants, till you have to fly in self-defence. The commandment to 'love one another' is replaced by the religion that teaches a withdrawal from all earthly things.

The only gesture of pity that I ever saw extended to the dogs of Lu-tai was based on even such a philosophy.

One hot summer's day, I was travelling between Peking and Mukden with Monsieur de Velde, editor of the *Courier de Pékin*. He is what we call an Old China Hand, one of those people whose long experience of the country has given them a feeling of proprietorship. From the moment when we left Peking, at half-past eight in the morning, Monsieur de Velde never stopped talking, and his conversation was mostly about the good old times, when there were no trains in China and one reached the capital in barges, those same barges that brought the tribute of rice to the Emperor along the Grand Canal.

Between Tientsin and Tang-ku he told me an extraordinary story about the railway that we were travelling on. It had been built by a private company in the 'nineties, to bring coal from the Kai-ping mines. Then the Chinese Government bought the whole concern, with no other object than to suppress it. They did not want railways in China. But though they continued to publish imperial edicts suppressing the railway, trains continued to run. The managing engineer was an Englishman, no other – if I was to believe Monsieur de Velde – than the original of Kipling's 'Stalky'. Whenever the Government inspectors appeared at Tang-ku to complain that trains were still running, he would prove to them that they must be misinformed, for the good reason that there were no engines! And no train, so he declared, could run without a locomotive of sorts. As a matter of fact, there was one engine, but whenever the Chinese Government's inspectors arrived at Tang-ku, it was nowhere to be seen. 'Stalky' (if it really were he) knew perfectly well when the inspectors would descend upon him, and used to bury the engine in a large hole expressly prepared for that purpose. He would dig it out again, when the inspectors left. Monsieur de Velde considered that this episode was typical of China at its best.

While our train was in the station at Tang-ku, he glared indignantly out of the carriage window at a little Chinese lady, wearing a silken jacket and trousers of the orthodox pattern, and a green woollen tam-o'-shanter of obvious foreign origin. She was having a heart-to-heart talk with a young Chinese traffic inspector, whose clothes were entirely foreign, from a felt hat, many sizes too large for him, to a pair of purple socks and patent-leather shoes.

'Who can she be, that female with the cap?' exclaimed Monsieur de Velde with a snort of contempt. 'Fifteen years ago, she would never have dared to put such a thing on her head. And as for that boy, if he had shown himself in the streets dressed like that, he would have been taken to the nearest *yamen* and given fifty strokes of the bamboo. But China to-day is no longer China, and what is worse, it is no longer amusing.'

Between Tang-ku and Lu-tai, the plain is covered with bushes which, as the autumn approaches, take on a wine-coloured tinge ('Lu-tai', in Chinese, means 'the terrace of marine grasses'). Sometimes, near the open sheets of water, one can see a heron, hunting for frogs or small crabs in the mud. The only signs of humanity are the little mounds of earth that show where some one has been buried, and the windmills that raise water into the reservoir of the Salt Gabelle. The heat on that plain, in the middle of the day in warm weather, is unbelievable; the damp air quivers above the reeds.

When we reached Lu-tai, Monsieur de Velde and I got out of the train to stretch our legs and get a breath of air. We were greeted, as usual, by a chorus of old women, shouting: 'Ta Laiè! Ta Laiè' from behind the wooden paling. And the dogs wandered about, as usual, under the railway carriages, while Monsieur de Velde continued talking:

'Have you ever noticed the dogs along the railway line in Siberia? They come to the stations from a considerable distance, in the hope of getting something from the station buffets, or from the restaurant cars. They are far more prosperous than the Chinese dogs, though it is much colder up there. Probably the Siberian dogs possess a master, whereas these poor brutes are merely street

132

scavengers, like the dogs in Constantinople in olden times. To tell the truth, I think the dogs here in Lu-tai are getting far too numerous.'

A poor bitch, whose protruding ribs reminded me of Doré's illustrations to the *Baron von Munchausen*, was sniffing the gravel close to my feet. The sight reminded me that I had in my pocket a packet of sandwiches, which the cook had prepared for my journey, and which I had not eaten, as Monsieur de Velde had insisted on my lunching with him in the restaurant car. I opened the parcel and dropped a sandwich near the famished dog. She gulped it down and continued sniffing at the gravel, without lifting her nose. Experience had taught her that such a windfall could only have come by accident. Unlike Oliver Twist, she never thought of asking for more.

'But this is a setter!'

The exclamation, in a tone of considerable surprise, came from Monsieur de Velde. I turned to discover what had interested him, and saw a dog, no less miserable than the others, who was trying to extract some nourishment from the empty shell of a sea-crab, which a traveller had thrown out of the window of a third-class carriage. These crabs are a speciality of the marshes along the coast. At Lu-tai there are always one or two itinerant vendors, who sell them ready cooked, on the platform.

The dog that Monsieur de Velde was looking at had a coat which, in other days, may have been silky, wavy and of a reddish colour flecked with white. But now it was the same colour as the dust under our feet, and covered with dirt and flies. Here and there the hair was missing and showed the sores that insects and malnutrition had engendered. One could see that the dog was very old. His eyes were rheumy, and when some one walked past him, along the platform, he would give a sudden start as if his senses had not warned him of the nearness of a human foot and therefore of the danger of being kicked.

133

Monsieur de Velde regarded him attentively:

'That is not a Chinese *wonk*,' he said. 'That is a well-bred dog. I should say an Irish setter.'

Certainly the dog's movements were not those of a *wonk*. Though ill-conditioned and suffering, he showed signs of race. Timid as he was, he lifted his half-blind eyes towards the carriage windows and to the travellers who leant out. Neither his own experience, nor that of his forefathers, had taught him that it was useless to ask for food from human beings. So he looked up and wagged his tail, to ingratiate himself with those who were his gods.

'Give alms to General Belisarius!' quoted Monsieur de Velde.

I threw the dog a sandwich. After swallowing it, he turned towards me and as I did not immediately give him another, instead of sniffing the ground as a *wonk* would have done, or whining like any other dog who begs, he threw himself down at my feet and stretched himself out stiffly.

Monsieur de Velde stared at him in astonishment. 'Some one must have taught him that trick,' he said. 'I once saw some English soldiers teaching a poodle to die for his country.'

'Or for the King,' I answered. 'Let's try him again.'

I gave the dog another sandwich. When he had eaten it, I said clearly: 'Good dog! Die for the King!'

The dog immediately threw himself down as before, and earned another sandwich.

'Poor brute!' exclaimed Monsieur de Velde. 'His master must have lost him while shooting snipe or wild duck in the marshes. And now he licks the empty crab shells in the station at Lu-tai. If he were younger and less diseased, I would take him with me. But he cannot have much longer to live. *Pauvre vieux tou-tou, viens!* I will spare you a few months of hunger and of pain.'

The unexpected report brought many faces, white and yellow, to the window of the railway carriages.

Monsieur de Velde had the habit of Old China Hands of always going armed. He put the small revolver back into his pocket and gazed at the body at his feet. This time the old dog had died indeed, though not 'for the King'. A little blood trickled from his nostril and from behind the ear.

A soldier drew near and said something that I did not understand. Probably he wished to know why we had shot that particular dog of all those on the platform. The beggar women stopped wailing, surprised at the sudden crack of a revolver. But seeing that nothing happened, they began again:

'Ta Laiè! Ta Laiè!'

Monsieur de Velde and I went back to our places in the train. The north breeze brought to us the sound of a whistle. The express from Mukden was signalled.

10 'Lieber Augustin'

I always thought that something strange must have happened at Shan-hai-kwàn, in the late summer of 1915 but *what* I could not say.

In recent years, the name of Shan-hai-kwàn has often figured in telegrams about Manchuria. But in 1915 there were very few people, out of China, who had ever heard of the place, and certainly no one, during the war, ever gave it a thought.

Shan means 'mountain'; *hai*, 'sea'; and *kwàn*, 'barrier'. The name Shan-hai-kwàn can be translated, 'The barrier of mountains and of sea'. The walled city is built at the foot of the outlying boulders of a big mountain range, which almost reaches the coast. An invading army, to pass southward from Manchuria into China, would have to thread its way along the narrow stretch of land between the hill-side and the sea-shore. In the seventeenth century, the Manchu tribes, seeking to penetrate into the territories then ruled over by the Ming emperors, were held up for thirty years by the 'barrier' of this small fortified town.

It is here that the Great Wall of China, which guards the northern marches for nearly two thousand miles over hill and dale, ends literally in the sea (the Chinese, who always seem to have the opposite view to ourselves, say that the Wall *begins* in the sea, rising in the waves, and ends in far Sin-kiang). Nowadays, the Wall serves only as a landmark and a monument to a past greatness. The path along the top, between Shan-hai-kwàn and the shore, is used as a secondary road to and from the town. People walk and ride along it in the cool of summer evenings.

Along the inner side of the Wall are old Chinese forts, which in 1900 were captured and taken over by the foreign troops coming to the rescue of the Legations. These forts are now used as summer quarters for the Legation Guards in Peking. At the extremity of the Wall, near the sea, is the British fort; next comes the Italian; then the French, and lastly the Japanese, which is the one nearest the town.

During the World War, these forts (all except the Japanese) were left in a state of complete abandonment. In the British fort there were only a few Baluchis of the Indian Army; tall, turbaned men who in their hours of liberty strolled about the woods or along the top of the wall, gravely saluting every foreigner and appropriating every chicken they happened to meet. The Italians were not more than a dozen sailors, with a petty officer. The French were a handful of elderly reservists, hastily recalled for local service, plus a company of Annamites, who had brought their wives and children with them from Indo-China.

Among these scanty representatives of what should have been a brilliant international garrison, the senior commandant was an English officer, Lieutenant Edward Harrison, who had been put in charge of the Baluchis at Shan-hai-kwàn, after the British Guard had departed for France or for the Dardanelles. To a healthily ambitious young officer, the fact of having been left behind as caretaker of a Chinese fort seemed little short of a catastrophe. Even the Baluchis felt the humiliation of being 'out of it' and expressed their wish to join the Sikhs who were fighting in Mesopotamia. Their lieutenant shared these views, though he urged his men to accept their lot with cheerfulness and did his best to keep them busy with the ordinary camp routine.

Harrison sought distraction in sport: sea-bathing,

riding, lawn tennis, long walks with a gun in search of snipe along the banks of the little river, or after duck on the marshy land along the coast. He sometimes made excursions among the hills, but his continual thirst for news from the front made him reluctant to absent himself for more than a few hours from Shan-hai-kwàn, where the English engineer who was in control of the railway received communication of the Reuter telegrams as they came in to Tientsin and Peking.

If Harrison had been in Japan, instead of in China, he might have found consolation in the company of Somebody-San. But the charms of the eternal feminine were lacking in Shan-hai-kwàn, and the natural beauties of sea and hill and forest had no attractions for one whose heart was in the trenches in Flanders.

The only companion with whom Harrison could while away the time was the senior French reservist, a man well known in China, though not in a military capacity, who, despite the rank of subaltern, recently conferred upon him, was generally spoken of as 'Père Antoine'. He was a Jesuit priest, engaged in geographical studies in the Far East. The responsibilities thrust upon him after the outbreak of the war were accepted by Père Antoine with Christian resignation. He excused himself with his superior officers for not knowing how to carry out their orders, and with his subordinates for not having the requisite experience to direct them. Despite these modest disclaimers, Père Antoine soon became an efficient officer. He knew his way about.

When I mentioned to him my suspicions that something must have happened at Shan-hai-kwàn in the summer of 1915, he shook his head.

'What makes you think that?' he asked.

'It is difficult to say. But I have an inkling. . . .'

'What could have happened? There was nobody there except Harrison and myself, and Harrison went home in September.'

'There was one other person whom I saw when I went

138

down for a few days' bathing. You knew him too: a German, or an Austrian. Some one told me that he was a prisoner escaped from Siberia. What became of him?'

'He left soon after Harrison. I believe he went to Tientsin and got interned with the other enemy subjects when China declared herself on the side of the Allies.'

'And nothing happened before he left?'

Père Antoine did not answer for a moment. Then he smiled and said:

'Nothing happened. But that nothing makes a strange story. If you like, I will tell you.'

To appreciate Père Antoine's narrative, it is necessary to know something about the man himself. Like most of the Jesuits who have their headquarters at the Zi-ca-wei observatory, near Shanghai, Père Antoine was an expert sinologue and a scientist of no mean repute. There was something comic in the idea of such a man figuring as a subaltern in command of a few reservists at Shan-hai-kwàn. But the history of the war is full of such anomalies.

His appearance was singular. A hooked nose, a goat-like beard, and a tendency of his blond-grey hair to curl behind the ears gave to him at times the appearance of a satyr. But no resemblance to the sylvan deity was apparent when you met the mildly benevolent gaze which Père Antoine turned on the world through a pair of steel-rimmed spectacles. Like Janus, he had two faces. There was something innocent and even saint-like in his expression, but the lines of his profile were sinister. I often wondered which of the two aspects represented the real man.

His conversation was kind and pleasant, showing a modest desire to receive information from all and sundry, and a willingness to place at their disposal the stores of his own vast knowledge. His manner lacked the martial quality which would have been in keeping with his uniform, and he often forgot to salute by raising his hand to his vizier. He would lift his cap or sun-helmet with gentle deference, revealing the tonsure beneath.

Harrison and Père Antoine had little in common, but they were constantly together. The Jesuit's quiet conversation had a soothing effect on the other's nerves. And Père Antoine found in his young companion a mine of information on those military matters of which he professed himself so ignorant.

One hot summer afternoon, shortly before sunset, Harrison and Père Antoine were seated side by side on the edge of one of the bastions that jutted out from the Great Wall, on its northern side. It was a good place to enjoy the view over the plain and the evening breeze off the sea. Telegrams that morning had brought news of another battle at the Dardanelles, and this, as usual, had provoked the bitter lamentations of the younger officer, to whom the hardships endured by his nationals recalled the bitterness of his own too comfortable lot. Père Antoine let him vent his feelings uninterrupted, and gazed over the fields of millet and Indian corn that stretched away between the sea-shore to the right and the mountain ranges to the left. Not far from where they sat the railway line emerged from a cutting in the Wall and disappeared towards the horizon in the direction of Mukden.

Along a narrow cart-track, among the millet fields, a little procession was moving in the direction of Shan-hai-kwàn, to the accompaniment of a primitive orchestra of gongs, pipes, and tabors.

'What are those people doing?' asked Harrison, as the breeze brought to his ears the sound of music.

Père Antoine was well informed as to local customs and ceremonies.

'They are returning from the shore,' he answered, 'where they have been to pray for rain, like the prophets of Baal, invoking false gods. That closed palanquin probably contains the image of the "grandfather" dragon who reigns over the rivers, the sea, and the clouds. The image has been down to the beach, where incense has been burnt and prayers recited. If rain comes the priests will claim a tithe of the harvest.'

'That music is not the usual Chinese music, surely? It sounds like a waltz tune, played on a flute.'

'You are right. It is odd. . . .'

Père Antoine gazed at the procession with a puzzled look on his face. Amid the crashing of the cymbals and the cries of the children who ran and skipped around the dragon, there rose a melody that was not Oriental. The beat of the drums and the deep note of a Chinese horn occasionally drowned that other sound, but when they ceased, the little melody rose again, clear and sweet as the song of a bird.

The last of the worshippers came in view, and with him the explanation. At the tail-end of the procession walked a man who, though dressed in the usual blue cotton of the Chinese peasants and shod like them, was obviously not a Chinese. He wore no hat, and his general appearance was extremely woebegone. But as he walked, he held a flute to his lips, and it was he who played the air which had puzzled the two men on the Wall. A big dog, which even in the distance looked tired and half-starved, limped wearily at the player's heels.

The cart-track, along which the procession was moving crossed the dry bed of a stream. On reaching its bank, the flute player stopped to look round while he put his instrument in his pocket. From where he stood he could see two people seated on the Wall, and he gazed at them, shading his face with his hand, for the sunlight was in his eyes. Then he detached himself from the procession and took a path that wandered through the grass.

The rubble fallen from the decaying masonry and sand brought by the wind formed a slope, up which it was possible to climb on to the Wall. Followed by the dog, the flute player made his way to a point only a few yards distant from where Harrison and Père Antoine were sitting, and he stood on a level with them.

141

Seen from near by, the wayfarer looked even more worn-out than he had appeared in the distance. His blue cotton clothes were in rags, and his Mongol shoes, made of felt, bore traces of blood. One eye was bound up, and the bandage was so dirty that it had not been visible from afar, for it was all of one colour with the grimy face. A reddish dust lay thick on the skin, on the hair, and on the ill-kept beard. He might have been a figure in terra-cotta, the only point of colour his unbandaged eye of a bright, clear blue.

With this one eye he stared down at the seated figures, and something in their appearance seemed to intimidate him, for he stepped back and seemed about to move off. But Père Antoine's benign glance must have been reassuring, as was the sight of his tonsure, which was visible, as he had laid his helmet beside him on the grass. The wayfarer made a gesture of salute and, speaking English with no trace of a foreign accent, he asked what was the name of the town that was visible in the distance.

'That,' answered Harrison, 'is Shan-hai-kwàn.'

'In China?' asked the wayfarer.

'In China, certainly. But, for the matter of that, Manchuria, whence you come, is a province of China.'

'So I have been told. But I confess that the sight of so many Russian and Japanese uniforms along the railway line did not reassure me as to the neutrality of the country through which I was travelling.'

'You are a belligerent?' asked Père Antoine.

'Yes. And, judging by your uniforms, we belong to different camps.'

'You are a German?' asked Harrison.

'No. An Austrian.'

'And how did you get here?'

'I was taken prisoner, about three months ago, in the Carpathians, and sent to Siberia. I jumped off the train and came here on foot, following the direction of the railway, but keeping well away from the track itself.'

'Well, I'm damned!'

'Jesus, Marie!'

Thus did his audience give expression to their astonishment. To have walked from Siberia to Shan-hai-kwàn meant to have crossed half Asia.

'And how did you manage for food?' asked Harrison.

'Kind people helped me, and one, whose name I never knew, gave me money and good advice. I did not fare so badly, as is proved by the fact that this dog insisted on attaching itself to me. I imprudently threw him a crust of bread. It must have been the first time that any one had ever offered him something. From that moment he never left me. Despite my reduced circumstances, I am still the master of his dreams.'

There was a hint of mockery in the wayfarer's voice and in the look of his blue eye. Père Antoine gazed at him with curiosity, and said:

'And what might your name be, if one may ask?'

'My name is Augustin Lieber, and I am a corporal in the Kaiserjäger of the Tyrol.'

For a moment Père Antoine looked puzzled and nonplussed. Then his face cleared and he smiled amiably.

'Augustin Lieber,' he repeated. 'Or shall we say *Lieber Augustin*? I see the allusion. In my youth I once stayed near Vienna, at the monastery of the Heilige Kreuz, and on spring days and Sundays I heard the students singing as they wandered in the woods. Unless I am mistaken, Lieber Augustin was the legendary vagabond, who played the flute, and to whom the Viennese attribute the invention of the waltz time which has ever since been their delight.'

Then, with a voice that did not lack melody, Père Antoine began to sing the air which they had heard a few minutes before, as the procession came up from the sea:

Ach, du lieber Augustin!
  Geld ist hin,
  Weib ist hin.
Ach, du lieber Augustin,
  Alles ist hin!

'They are not verses,' he added, 'that a cleric should repeat. But the uniform that I am wearing allows me a certain licence. At all events, sir, we will respect your incognito and the name you choose to bear. I only know one other that might suit you so well. It is Wotan, the one-eyed wanderer. But you must be tired, and doubt-less hungry. My ecclesiastical calling will justify my offering hospitality to an enemy, should you wish to rest and refresh yourself at my house.'

At this point Harrison hastened to intervene.

'Although I am not called upon, by reason of my pro-fession, to succour all those who are in trouble, I would be happy to offer hospitality to an enemy in distress, seeing that it has not been my good fortune to meet him in the field.'

The wayfarer regarded them with his unbandaged eye, and smiled.

'In this generous competition,' he said, 'it falls to me to award the prize. May I be guided by material considera-tions? It is true that I am tired and very hungry. I will accept the invitation of whoever lives nearest.'

'I do! I do!' exclaimed Harrison and Père Antoine in perfect synchronism.

'Look! My house is behind those trees,' added Père Antoine.

'My house is there, where you see the flag,' said Harrison.

The wayfarer laughed.

'Far be it from me,' he said, 'to doubt the word of one who is both soldier and priest. But it so happens that his house is not visible from here, whereas the flag is. And it marks a place of refuge. For that reason I choose, sir, to be your guest.'

The wayfarer looked at Harrison and bowed. It almost seemed as if, in spite of his woebegone appearance, he was conscious of conferring an honour.

After having accompanied the other two as far as the entrance to the British fort, Père Antoine returned to his own quarters. He was one of those methodical people who keep a diary (at a later date he showed me a few pages). On the evening of Lieber Augustin's arrival the event was recorded as follows:

'There arrived here to-day on foot an Austrian, escaped (so he says) from a train transporting prisoners to Siberia. He is evidently a personage of high standing, and gives a false name "Lieber Augustin". He says he is only a corporal of the Kaiserjäger.

'This is the first escaped prisoner with whom I have had the opportunity of conversing. One might learn something from him concerning the organization which the enemy has set up in order to facilitate the escape of prisoners from Siberia.

'It is perhaps a pity that L.A. should be the guest of Harrison, and not mine.'

Lieber Augustin remained for a few days at the British fort, recovering his health, which the hardships of the long march had impaired. He wore his host's clothes, which suited him well enough, for they were of the same height and build. They both had fair hair, and though the Austrian was the elder of the two, he showed it less in his physical traits than in a certain air of assured authority. He trimmed his beard, and after a day or two he discarded the bandage over his eye (which was affected with a slight conjunctivitis).

He wrote various letters to Tientsin and Peking and received answers addressed to Mr. A. Lieber. These answers contained remittances of money, with which he made a trip to Tientsin, to refurnish his wardrobe and to procure various necessities.

He might have stayed with the Austrian naval detachment in Peking (which acted as the Legation Guard), but he preferred to return to Shan-hai-kwàn, where he took up his abode in a temple in the hills, with a 'boy' recommended by Père Antoine, a cook, two coolies, and his dog. The custom of living in temples is so widespread in

China that Lieber Augustin's presence there provoked no comment.

Like other subjects of the Central Powers before China saw fit to abandon neutrality, Lieber Augustin was not 'interned', but he was cut off from his fatherland. Unless with a false passport, it was impossible for him to return to Austria. Land and sea routes were controlled by the Allies. The fact of his having come back to Shan-hai-kwàn showed that he nourished no hope of returning to the front.

Lieber Augustin and Harrison found themselves in a similar situation. Both longed to go to Europe, to take part in the war, but to both it was denied, and this served to enhance a mutual sympathy, born at their first encounter. The fact of belonging to opposing belligerent armies gave to their incipient friendship a touch of paradox, but could not diminish the kindly feeling. Père Antoine also remained on good terms with the escaped prisoner, but unlike Harrison, never became his boon companion.

During the first eight months of the war, Lieber Augustin had fought on the Austro-Russian front. When speaking of his own part in the campaign, he was careful not to reveal his rank, but the Englishman found in him an inexhaustible source of that specialized form of knowledge which only first-hand experience can give and only a commanding officer could possess. By tacit consent they made no allusion to political questions. They would talk of the difficulties of campaigning in a mountainous country, of new systems of fortification, and of the new-fangled art of camouflage.

'I used to think I was rather good at camouflage,' said Lieber Augustin. 'But that may be only because I was fighting against the Russians, who were no good at it at all!'

'I don't think that I would shine at it,' observed Père Antoine. 'I never succeed in looking anything but a priest camouflaged as a soldier.'

'The best camouflage of all,' said Harrison, 'would be to make yourself look like a soldier of the enemy's camp. Though I suppose it might lead to trouble with your own side.'

These conversations would take place in Harrison's private quarters and less often up at the temple that Lieber Augustin occupied on the mountain-side. The choice of such a residence showed that he belonged indeed to a famous regiment of Alpine troops. The climb up to his temple was both steep and long. But the view from the eyrie was sufficient compensation. To the east the eye could travel along the sea-coast to the little port of Chin-wang-tao, where coaling steamers lay at anchor. To the west, that is to say, inland, one could follow the line of the Great Wall, up over the hills and down into the valleys. The little river that had its outlet in the sea close to the British fort emerged on to the plain from among those mountains and flowed far below Lieber Augustin's temple. At sunset, the red sky was reflected in curving waters between precipitous banks. There was a terrace in front of the temple. It was there that Lieber Augustin passed most of his time, reading or playing the flute.

A few pieces of furniture had been brought from Tient-sin: a camp-bed, a cupboard, some tables, and chairs. A note of luxury was struck by a large carpet, spread over the Chinese *kang* and attached on one side half-way up the wall. It was a fine carpet, yet Lieber Augustin allowed his dog to sleep on it.

Two ponies, stabled in a farm half-way to the town, were used by Lieber Augustin to make excursions in the surrounding country. He had also bought a gun, with which he used to wander in the hills or go duck-shooting with Harrison in the marshes by the sea.

During the summer months, Lieber Augustin would come down daily from his temple and bathe with Harrison. They used to swim out to a sand-bank which ran parallel to the shore. Père Antoine would join them on the beach, but he was no swimmer.

* * *

Summer passed and the millet grew ripe for the harvest. The rust-coloured tufts on their tall stalks gave a brownish tinge to the landscape north and south of the Wall. The Indian corn was already cut and the golden cobs lay out to dry on the roofs of the cottages.

At the beginning of September, Harrison received orders to return to Europe and to report himself at headquarters in Flanders. Although the last month of his stay in Shan-hai-kwàn had been less tedious than the former ones, the sudden call to arms filled him with a satisfaction that he made no attempt to conceal. Père Antoine was the first person to whom Harrison gave the news of his recall. The Frenchman expressed his congratulations, and then added:

'I suppose you could not keep the reason of your departure a secret? Why not say that you are leaving for Shanghai, and then write back later to say good-bye?'

'Why so much mystery?'

'I was thinking of our Austrian friend. It might be better if he did not know.'

Harrison shook his head. 'Even if I did not tell him, he would find out at once from some one else.'

This was so true that, even before Harrison saw Lieber Augustin again, he received a note from him, of one word only: 'Congratulations.' But for many days the Austrian did not come down, as usual, to bathe on the shore.

When Lieber Augustin had first settled in his temple on the hill, Père Antoine had found him a Chinese 'boy' and a cook. The latter was brother to the cook of the French detachment. These two worthies used to meet daily at the market in Shan-hai-kwàn, and, like servants all over the world, they would gossip over their masters.

Père Antoine used to practise the Chinese spoken language with his servants, and through them received all sorts of information that to other and less methodical people might have seemed insignificant. After the arrival of the telegram for Harrison's recall, Père Antoine encouraged his boy and his cook to bring him

148

any news that they might collect concerning the doings of the 'foreign devil' who lived up at the temple on the hill. In Père Antoine's diary for the first days of September 1915, Lieber Augustin's doings are often mentioned:

'*September 1st.* Weather cooler. News of L.A. (as told by cook): Master very sad; yesterday stay all day on terrace; look at view, smoke, eat very little; play flute.

'*September 2nd.* Weather fine. News of L.A. Master very sad; last night no sleep; this morning send off letter to Tientsin.

'*September 5th.* Rain. News of L.A. Master receive telegram. Less sad, but no sleep much. Allo time walk up and down terrace.

'*September 6th.* Weather fine, much cooler. News of L.A. Master go shoot in mountains. Takee dog. Other times no takee dog; he no good for shooting. To-day dog run after hare when Master fire gun; dog dead. Master very sad.'

On the seventh of September Lieber Augustin went down to Shan-hai-kwàn to see Harrison and Père Antoine. He told them of the accident to the dog, and seemed very sorry about it. He showed a friendly interest in Harrison's preparations for his journey, saying that he wished to see him off. He also said that he would come down to the shore, during the next few days, to bathe.

By that time Harrison was almost ready to start. He had been to Tientsin to do some shopping and to get his military passport. He proposed sailing from Chin-wang-tao to Shanghai on a steamer belonging to the Kailan mining company, and then to embark on a Japanese liner which would take him to Marseilles. The distance from Shan-hai-kwàn to Chin-wang-tao is about sixteen miles, and Harrison had decided to proceed thither by the morning train, although his steamer was not scheduled to arrive in port till late at night. But Lieber Augustin offered to lend him a pony and to ride with him to

Chin-wang-tao, if he preferred to go in the afternoon. Harrison accepted and they arranged to bathe and to pass the day together before starting.

The date fixed for Harrison's departure was the tenth of September. To avoid the heat, he arranged to leave Shan-hai-kwàn a little before sunset, and, profiting by Lieber Augustin's offer of ponies, to accomplish the greater part of the journey by moonlight (the moon was then at its full). His luggage was sent off by rail, to be taken on board by the employees of the mining company. There were no other preparations, and Harrison could pass the last afternoon with his two friends, as in the days before the fateful telegram had arrived calling him to Europe. They lunched together at Père Antoine's house and remained there till about four o'clock. Then they walked down to the shore for a bathe.

Père Antoine went too, but he did not bathe. He sat down on the sand and watched his two friends swim out to the sand-bank, while he filled his pipe for a smoke. But when he felt in his pockets for matches he discovered that he had left them at home. Both Harrison and Lieber Augustin were smokers, so he decided to look for a match-box in the pockets of their clothes, which they had left in the bathing hut. The pockets of Harrison's jacket were bulging with papers, for he had brought with him his passport, his tickets, and money. Père Antoine did not wish to touch these precious documents, so he searched for a match in the pockets of Lieber Augustin. Strangely enough, these also were full and bulging. Père Antoine first took out the flute in two pieces, then a pair of scissors wrapped in paper, then a safety razor and a tube of cream labelled *Euxesis*, which could be used (according to the directions printed on the outside) for shaving without soap and water. Père Antoine contemplated these objects in some surprise. A moment later he returned to sit down on the sand. He had not found matches and his pipe was still unlit.

As soon as the swimmers returned to shore, Père

Antoine took leave of them with many expressions of regret. He explained that he had a bad headache and wished to go home, to lie down. Harrison was surprised, but bade him good-bye, with vigorous handshakes and the hope that they might meet again. It came over him suddenly how fond he had grown of this quiet-mannered, modest man in his unaccustomed uniform.

It was past six o'clock and the sun was drawing near the top of the mountain ranges, when Harrison and Lieber Augustin mounted their ponies and started for Chin-wang-tao. They followed a path along the bank of the river. Less than a mile from the British fort was a wooden bridge, and it was towards this that they made their way, putting their ponies to a trot. Harrison rode on ahead, followed by Lieber Augustin at a distance of about ten yards. To their left was the stream, its waters stilled by the pressure of the incoming tide. To the right were the woods, with frequent clearings made by the Chinese, who are always seeking more room for their crops. On the other side of the river there were no woods, but only the millet fields. Through these fields the path followed the line of the coast towards Chin-wang-tao.

On reaching the bridge (a frail construction, built to carry a trolley line across the stream), the two riders came unexpectedly upon a little group of French soldiers under a corporal. They were mounted on ponies and appeared to be waiting for somebody. The corporal was a middle-aged man with a grey moustache. He rode up to Harrison and saluted him, holding out a letter, neatly typewritten on the official paper of the French detachment, but without an envelope. Not a little surprised, Harrison took the missive and read it. It contained a brief message from Père Antoine:

'CHER AMI, You will give great pleasure to me and to my five comrades, if you will allow them to escort you to Chin-wang-tao.

'I am sure you will not refuse me this last request.

'Yours ever,
'PÈRE ANTOINE'

The offer of an escort was a friendly, if formal, courtesy that Harrison had not expected. He said a few words of thanks to the corporal and his men, and while declaring himself much flattered and accepting their company with great pleasure, he strove to quiet his pony, which was impatient of the delay and turned and pawed the ground. The group, which now consisted of seven horsemen, crossed the bridge and set off in Indian file along the path among the millet fields.

The sun had set behind the mountains, which had taken on a violet tinge and stood out darkly against the gold and rose colour of the sky. Frogs croaked along the river-bank and a cloud of midges circled above the water.

A figure that had been hidden behind a group of willows emerged from the deeper shadows. Père Antoine went and stood on the bridge, leaning his elbows on the wooden parapet. There was something ghostly in his sudden appearance, and the evening light showed his satyr-like profile. It was as if the great god Pan had stepped out of the reeds in the river-bed, where he had lain in waiting for passers-by. And, indeed, after a few minutes a wayfarer appeared on the path, along which Harrison and his companions had started. It was Lieber Augustin, alone and on foot, walking with bent head and leading his pony, the rein held loosely over one arm. On reaching the bridge, he saw Père Antoine and stopped.

'How is it that you have come back?' asked Père Antoine.

'Like you, I had a headache, and Harrison does not lack company. What made you think of giving him an escort?'

Père Antoine pointed in the direction of Chin-wang-tao.

'The millet stalks are high,' he said. 'So high that they hide even a man on horseback. During the autumn campaign of the Liao Yang, in the Russo-Japanese war, the

152

wounded were often abandoned in the fields, for it was impossible to find them all.'

'What has that to do with Harrison and me?'

'Harrison carried his passport, and money and tickets for his journey. If he had remained hidden, like the wounded on the Liao Yang, to die among the millet fields, it would have been easy for some one – especially for some one of the same height and build, and with fair hair like his – to have taken his place on the steamer.'

'If you allude to me, I may point out that I wear a beard and moustache.'

'If you carried a razor and some shaving cream, it would be easy to take them off.'

Lieber Augustin did not answer and did not seem perturbed. He felt in his pocket and brought out, not the razor, but his flute, in two pieces, which he slowly screwed together. For a few moments longer he remained there in silence, looking down at the water. Then with a nod of farewell he started off again along the path towards Shan-hai-kwàn, his pony ambling gently by his side. As they disappeared among the willows, the breeze brought back to Père Antoine, standing once more alone on the bridge, the melody that he and Harrison had heard on that summer evening on the Wall:

Ach, du lieber Augustin!
  Geld ist hin,
  Weib ist hin!
Ach, du lieber Augustin,
  Alles ist hin!

And that is what Père Antoine meant when he said that nothing had happened in Shan-hai-kwàn in the late summer of 1915.

I wonder if *he* knew who Lieber Augustin really was?

11   The Captain's Dog

In J.O.P. Bland's *Houseboat Days in China* (a book containing more Eastern lore than its title would lead you to suppose), there is a chapter entitled 'On the hypnotic influence of the P'utzu.' The idea is that the embroidered squares, as worn by Mandarins of the old régime on the back and chest, had a hypnotic influence especially potent in the case of foreign diplomats, who never failed to fall under the spell.

I do not wish to go into the matter of the P'utzu, but I have noticed that the same effects are produced on the minds of foreigners by nothing more formidable than a Pekinese dog. Owners of other species may be dog-ridden, but never do they reach such depths of abjection as when they are possessed by a Pekinese. The verse from Isaiah (ii. 9) that Mr. Bland puts at the head of his chapter on the P'utzu, is no less applicable to a Pekinese dog's attitude towards humanity in general and his own master (or mistress) in particular: 'And the mean man boweth down, and the great man humbleth himself: therefore forgive them not.'

The Chinese have a legend about this breed. They tell a story of a lion who fell in love with a squirrel. Realizing that their different sizes constituted an impediment to matrimony, he consulted a magician. The latter offered to make the lion so small that the course of true love might run smooth. But the lion objected that, if he dwindled to the size of a squirrel, he would lose in dignity. The magician assured him that even this difficulty could be overcome, and he cast a spell over the lion, reducing him to the required size. Yet, strange to say, he still boasted all the dignity of the King of Beasts. And this was the first Pekinese.

If the Chinese *wonks*, such as those that frequent the station at Lu-tai, represent the lowest rung in the canine social scale, no doubt but that the 'Palace dogs' (as they are called in Peking) are the cream of good society, and expect to be treated as such. More than any other dog, they impose their own proud conception of themselves upon a long-suffering humanity.

There was once a relation of Uncle Podger's (to be precise, his first cousin) who was bred by my own *k'ai-men-ti*, in the porter's lodge, just as Uncle Podger was. Later on he was given (Kuniang was mixed up in the matter in some way) to the captain of the Italian destroyer *Etruria*, who took him away to Shanghai. The story of his subsequent activities reached me indirectly through a correspondence with the ship's doctor, who formerly had been in the Italian Legation Guard in Peking, and at that time used to attend Kuniang.

The dog's name was Pao, which is Chinese for 'treasure'.

At the beginning of the Great War the *Etruria* was stationed in Chinese waters and the captain, Pao's master, was no less popular in the cosmopolitan society of the Treaty Ports than he was with the officers and men of his ship. Like that noted character of the *Bab Ballads*, Captain Reece of the *Mantelpiece*,

> He was adored by all his men,
> For worthy Captain Reece, R.N.,
> Did all that lay within him to
> Promote the comfort of his crew.

But the arrival of Pao had the effect of diminishing, if not the captain's popularity, at least his prestige. The doctor (a good fellow, but addicted to grumbling) observed that from that day the *Etruria* was transformed into a floating kennel, and her captain trotted round like a dog. This unkind remark was provoked by the departure of Pao and his master in the captain's launch (the *Etruria* was then in harbour at Hong-Kong) in search of a manicure, whose services were required, not by the captain himself, but by his dog.

It was enough to look at Pao in order to understand the fundamental principles from which the art of China has evolved. In his small body were united elements which appear in Chinese sculpture, pictures, and porcelain. Although everything about him, from nose to tail, was crooked, yet in that crookedness there was a harmonious grace. His backbone took a curve that gave him a concave appearance, like a boat on shore, resting on trestles. His coat was black, and the only touch of colour about him was his pink tongue, which was always hanging out.

He had large protruding eyes, but his eyesight was poor. An Englishman with much knowledge of dogs explained to the captain that the peculiar formation of a Pekinese's head rendered him liable, more than other dogs, to a lesion of the optic nerve, owing to the habit, common among owners of little dogs, of lifting them up by the scruff of the neck. This method of ascent was dangerous with prominent eyes like Pao's. If, after learning this, the captain had caught any of his subordinates lifting Pao up by the scruff of the neck, the culprit would certainly have been made to walk the plank.

The fact of being black conferred a special immunity upon Pao when the ship was coaling (the *Etruria* was an old vessel and did not burn oil). He was the only creature on board who on these occasions did not alter his appearance. But however clean he might seem, he did in fact collect upon himself an incredible amount of black dust, which he distributed impartially on his master's clothes and furniture. At Saigon, where the French Governor came on board, the captain left his cabin hurriedly to receive the official visit, bearing two black paw-marks on his white uniform, an inch or two below his decorations.

Another of Pao's peculiarities was that he had no voice. When excited or annoyed, he looked as if he might be barking; his little body was violently convulsed, but no sound issued from his mouth. The captain spoke of this as 'Pao's aphonia', and appeared convinced that it was a sure sign of good breeding, an opinion which nobody ventured to contradict.

According to a legend that accompanied Pao, when he first went on board the *Etruria*, he was the last scion of a noble line, belonging to the Manchu emperors. The fall of the 'Great Pure' dynasty threatened to bring about the extinction of its dogs. The Empress Dowager owned the last surviving couple. After the death of Tzu-hsi, a eunuch stole her dogs, and fearing that their grotesque appearance would reveal their *sangre azul*, he confided them in secrecy to the *k'ai-men-ti* at the Shuang Liè Ssè. Subsequently the eunuch died, and the imperial breed continued in the humble surroundings of a porter's lodge. I may add (if the story is true, which I doubt) that they multiplied exceedingly.

Conversation on board the *Etruria* after Pao's arrival turned frequently upon the subject of dogs. The ship's officers had travelled much in foreign lands and some of them were gifted with lively imaginations. The supply of doggy anecdotes was assured for a long time. The following sample is given in the words of the officer who told it:

'A friend of mine, a diplomat, had a German dachshund, one of those very long dogs with bowed legs. He was called Jim, but when he accompanied his master on an important mission to Constantinople, his name was changed for local use into the more pompous one of Jim-barkey Bey. One day he was run over by a motor-car and broke his front legs. The vet put them into splints, or into plaster of Paris – I forget which – but, anyway, he mended them. Unfortunately he set them straight, like

157

the legs of other dogs, instead of crooked, like curved lines including a parenthesis. So when he got well, poor Jim-barkey Bey was higher in front than behind, and looked like a small giraffe.'

'Do you think it would be possible to get a photograph of that dog?' asked the doctor. But the narrator was busy lighting a cigar and paid no attention.

When Italy entered the war, in May 1915, the *Etruria* received orders to proceed to the Red Sea, and for many months was engaged in bombarding Turkish garrisons along the Arabian coast, in searching suspected ships, and in the capture of those which were convicted of carrying contraband.

It was very hot in the Red Sea, and the *Etruria* was like a floating kitchen range. The ship was permanently cleared for action, and the awnings, together with all fittings that were not indispensable, were left at Massaua. So the sun beat down on the decks from dawn until sunset. The decks were of iron, and so was the furniture in the cabins, even to the drawers in the chests. The plans for the construction of the *Etruria* had been based on the experience gained during the Spanish-American war. The deck of a Spanish ship had been set on fire by the bursting of a shrapnel, and for several years after the naval construction departments of various countries built their ships entirely of metal, with the result that, in hot climates, they were uninhabitable.

'I feel as if I were living in an oven for roasting chestnuts,' said the doctor, mopping his brow for the twentieth time in the space of five minutes.

The sufferings inflicted by the *Etruria* on the enemy appeared as nothing when compared to those undergone by her own officers and crew, while patrolling a barren coast, plumb on the heat equator. The captain did his best to alleviate his own misery and that of his men, but even the methods of Captain Reece were inadequate on the Red Sea between June and September.

158

Did they with thirst in summer burn?
Lo, seltzogenes at every turn,
And on all very sultry days
Cream ices handed round on trays.

When her duties did not impose some particular course, the *Etruria* steamed against the wind, but often that was not possible. Then, with a following breeze, officers and men would go about their work with purple congested faces which were positively alarming. The doctor had hidden all the thermometers, so that the physical sufferings caused by the heat should not be increased by the knowledge of the actual temperature. In sandy bays along the coast the sun reverberated on the arid hills and the air trembled dizzily.

Even readers who are familiar with major operations in the Great War may not be so well informed as to what happened year by year in the Red Sea. Indeed, some of the facts represent an item of secret naval history.

When Turkey joined the fray on the side of the Central Powers, in the autumn of 1914, there was a small Turkish gunboat in the Red Sea. This ship, which was called the *Ferid*, was almost as much of a joke in Near Eastern ports as the old Spanish *Terror del Mundo* had been in the Pacific, during the years that preceded the Spanish-American war. Not only the ship was antiquated; so was her commanding officer. The captain of the *Ferid*, despite the modest rank of *Lieutenant de Vaisseau*, as indicated on his visiting cards (which led one to expect a certain youthfulness), was seventy-five years old: a relic of the Sultan's navy, who had been kept on, or forgotten, by the Young Turks. As was customary in the Turkish navy, he lived on board with his wife, who was some twenty years younger than he. The *Ferid* and her aged captain were well known in naval circles, and when Turkey entered the war, all British and French battleships in Eastern waters set out to look for them. But they had completely disappeared! This fact caused a certain uneasiness, for it seemed likely that a second *Emden* might begin operating east of Suez. Though the *Ferid* could hardly be considered formidable, even an old gunboat can do a lot of damage disorganizing merchant shipping.

The initial alarm subsided as time went on and the *Ferid* gave no sign of life. It was supposed that the aged captain, in view of the utter hopelessness of his position, had scuttled his ship and sunk her, landing in boats in some small Eastern port with his wife and crew. A less charitable hypothesis pictured him as having sold the ship, either entire or in pieces, and to be living somewhere on the proceeds.

And then suddenly the news was flashed from port to port and from ship to ship that the *Ferid* had been sighted in the Straits of Perim and had stopped a French steamer that was making for Jibuti, requisitioning all her stores.

This occurred in April 1915. But when the *Etruria* arrived in those waters at the beginning of June, the Turkish gunboat had disappeared once more and the mystery as to her whereabouts was deeper than ever.

Meanwhile, with the advancing summer, the heat was becoming more and more intense, and the one to suffer most on the *Etruria* was Pao. The scorching decks burned his feet, and the suffocating atmosphere in the cabins deprived him of sleep. Drops rolled incessantly off his pink tongue (it was his way of perspiring), and every crooked line in his little body revealed an internal discomfort. The ship's doctor regarded him suspiciously, fearing that he might develop hydrophobia. Once, when the *Etruria* escorted a captured ship carrying contraband to Massaua, Pao was sent up to the plateau of Asmara for a breath of fresh air. But when he returned on board after those few days of respite he seemed more depressed than ever.

At last he got sunstroke and for three days the captain

walked about with Pao in his arms, holding an ice-bag against his head. The doctor said something about 'softening of the brain', but it was not clear whom he was referring to.

To every one's astonishment, Pao recovered; or, at least, he returned to his former state of acute misery; but there was no doubt that another month of the Red Sea would kill him. The captain was so genuinely distressed that the doctor was touched and suggested that Pao's health might be improved if he could partake of a little fresh grass. He added:

'We might be able to grow some grass in a flower-pot or a wooden box filled with earth; that is to say, if we watered it continually.'

'A very good idea,' agreed the captain. 'But first we must get some grass, and I doubt if on all the coast of the Red Sea there is a single blade.'

'I saw some half-way between Massaua and Asmara,' said the doctor. 'At Ghinda there is plenty.'

'That may be, but unless we capture another ship with contraband, there can be no possible excuse for returning just now to Massaua.'

'I know where you can find some,' said the second in command. 'In the Bay of Annesley, not far from Zula. When I was on board the *Saetta* I went on land there, for some shooting. Near a spring, not far from the shore, I saw some grass.'

'What is there to shoot thereabouts?' asked the doctor.

'Panthers and some lions, small ones without manes. They are of a reddish colour, like the soil.'

'Better be careful. Pao might share the fate of the martyrs in the Colosseum.'

'We could send him on shore under a strong escort,' said the captain.

After some hesitation, the cruise to the Bay of Annesley in search of grass was undertaken. This was not the official reason given for the expedition. The necessity was

161

alleged of searching for Turkish sampans. It is true that those shores were in the Italian colony of Eritrea, but the owners of sampans are bold men, who do not fear to venture within the territorial waters of an enemy.

Dawn was breaking when the *Etruria's* prow cut the still waters of the bay. Although the heat was abnormal, even at that early hour, the doctor was sleeping peacefully. He was awakened by the firing of a cannon.

'They must be firing at the lions,' he grunted as he turned over, hoping to recapture sleep. 'Or perhaps it is to keep them at a distance while Pao eats his grass.'

Another gun boomed above his head, and he heard the voice of some one passing his cabin door:

'Think of choosing this spot to come and hide in!'

'What on earth is it all about?' grumbled the doctor, and getting out of his bunk, he went and looked through a porthole. In the distance he saw the grey line of the coast and near by a group of red rocks, among which was anchored a small ship of curious appearance, without masts or funnels. Indeed, he would not have recognized it as a ship at all if there had not been a figure standing on what might have been the bridge, waving a white flag.

The doctor hurried into his uniform and ran up on deck, where he found the second in command.

'What ship is that?' he asked.

'The *Ferid*. She must have been hiding in the shelter of those rocks, off and on, since the beginning of the war.'

'Where are her funnels?'

'They must have removed them, and they have painted her the same colour as the rocks. Even her lines have been changed. See the shape of her bows? It looks to me like a pile of baskets, covered over with a painted sail cloth. Had we not come to this side of the bay to look for grass, we might never have known she was here. Even from inside the bay one might never notice. I suppose that the fishermen hereabouts have been paid to keep silence.'

'It looks as if she has surrendered.'

'Yes. After two shots. And perhaps even those were not necessary.'

At that moment the captain came down from the bridge, accompanied by Pao, who seemed much cheered by the prospect of going ashore. He went through the movements of barking, but without producing any sound.

'What a piece of luck,' said the captain, 'that we put in here! A pretty figure we should have cut if it had been discovered later that a Turkish gunboat had remained undisturbed in Italian waters till the conclusion of the war.'

When the formalities of surrender were over, one or two sailors were sent on shore to procure grass for Pao. Unfortunately, they could not find any. But later, when the *Etruria* escorted the captured gunboat to Massaua, Pao was sent up to Ghinda, where he remained till the end of the war. The discovery and capture of the *Ferid* were attributed to the perspicacity of Pao's master. Only a few people knew that the expedition to the Bay of Annesley was intended to procure grass for a Pekinese dog.

12 The Inn of Perpetual Misfortune

In justice to Mr. Tang, I must admit that for one short story (and that pure fiction) which he once induced me to tear up, there have been many true ones that I would never have written if he had not put me on their track.

On one occasion I mentioned to him that I had heard of a Chinese inn called 'The Inn of Perpetual Misfortune'. He gave a snort of contempt and answered that it was nonsense: no hostelry in China could do business with such an unlucky name.

'Who told you of it?' he asked.

'A student-interpreter of the American Legation,' I answered. 'He passed a night there on the way to Jehol. It is not on the road that goes by the Tung Ling, but in some village more to the west.'

'That would be on the old road. But I do not believe it. He must have misunderstood. These student-interpreters are all the same. As soon as they begin to distinguish a few of the radicals, they think they have discovered China. *Fu* means good fortune or bad, according to the tone in which it is pronounced. Probably the name is Yung Fu Tien. Your student-interpreter translates it Eternal Misfortune Inn. Instead of which it means exactly the opposite.'

'But my friend showed me the characters. The middle one is not *Fu* but *Hen*. The hotel is called Yung Hen Tien. I understand that *Hen* means "hatred", "malignity", "anger". One might call it "The Inn of Perpetual Hatred", but the evil significance is unmistakable. It seems to me that "The Inn of Perpetual Misfortune" is not a bad translation.'

Mr. Tang was not convinced. He went away muttering: 'Yung Hen Tien. Rubbish!'

The next time I saw him he made no mention of the matter. But some weeks later he came to me with a sheepish expression, to make *amende honorable*. The inn *did* exist. He told me how and why.

Once upon a time there was a court eunuch who became the ruler of China. His name was Liu-li-tè. Like Pier delle Vigne, he held *del cor di Federigo ambo le chiavi*. He had submitted the will of the Emperor to his own. The Son of Heaven saw only through the eyes of his chief eunuch, heard with his ears, and spoke through his mouth. The guardian of the harem spoke like Cardinal Wolsey: *Ego et rex meus*.

Liu-li-tè was so rich that most of the pawnshops in the capital and all those in his native town belonged to him. A great part of the tribute from the provinces, in furs, in silks, and in pearls, was stored in his house. But as often happens to those who rule through the favour of the great, the eunuch's star began to wane. A war that ended badly, an imperial concubine thwarted in her ambitions, calumnies of jealous rivals – such were the causes of his downfall. Even his life was in danger.

He was left behind in Peking when the court went to Jehol for the autumn hunting. This was a blow to him and a triumph for his adversaries. It added to his danger, for it kept him away from the Son of Heaven.

In that garden of Klingsor that is called the Summer Palace, Liu-li-tè paced the peony terraces and trembled at the arrival of every courier from Jehol. He had a friend who sent him confidential reports about what was happening in the entourage of the Emperor, and these reports described the situation in gloomy tints which not all the euphemism of the Chinese epistolary style could brighten. *Les absents ont toujours tort*, and

Liu-li-tè's rivals were consolidating their ascendancy over the Emperor, while the chief eunuch was not there to counteract their influence.

Impatient and impulsive by nature, Liu-li-tè felt he could not bear to remain in Peking till the court returned, and he decided to make one more attempt to reconquer the imperial favour. In former days his bolder coups had ever gained the approval of the Son of Heaven. In spite of the order to remain in the capital, he decided to go to Jehol. He hoped that once in the presence, he could plead his cause in such a way as to confound his enemies.

The journey by cart, from Peking to Jehol, takes about four days. On the evening of the third day Liu reached a village called Wang-cha-chai ('the palisade of the Wang family'), and he decided to pass the night there, at the inn which in those days was called Yung Fu Tien, 'The Inn of Perpetual Good Fortune'. It so happened that on the same day a group of actors, attached to the court, were returning to Peking after giving a series of performances at Jehol.

They were the most famous actors in the empire, and naturally would never have condescended to show themselves in such a small village as Wang-cha-chai. But, having learnt of the arrival of the chief eunuch, who was still considered the virtual ruler of China, they hurriedly unloaded their carts, unpacked their bundles, and selected their finest costumes. The local mandarin and his subordinates, not to mention the rustic inhabitants of Wang-cha-chai, were beside themselves with excitement. A recital by actors of the court, in costumes worn before the Emperor himself: O truly auspicious day! O happy owner of the inn, aptly named of Perpetual Good Fortune; the inn which could now boast of having worthily welcomed the Tai-dien, the First Imperial Eunuch!

The programme of the evening's entertainment announced two dramas, of which the first bore the title *Kung Cheng Chi* (the stratagem of the empty city). As the reader may not know the story, I will give him a brief synopsis:

'In the days of the Three Kingdoms, the Duke Chu-ke-liang, at the head of a large army, invaded the Kingdom of Wei. But his generals showed themselves inefficient and undisciplined, so it happened that the Duke found himself separated from his army in the small town of Si Cheng. He had only a few troops with him, whereas the enemy was approaching in force, under the orders of Sze Ma Chi. So the Duke had recourse to a stratagem. He ordered his scanty troops to leave him and the gates of the town to be opened wide. He then went up on to a tower above the open gate, and sat there in view of those who were approaching the town. Beside him were two young girls, one of whom played the lute, while the other served tea. When Sze Ma Chi drew near and observed this scene, he was filled with doubts. Suspecting an ambuscade, he would not enter the town.

'Later, the Duke succeeded in rejoining his army, and returned safely to his own country.'

Though summer was over, the weather was still warm, and the evening's performance took place in an outer courtyard, near the entrance to the inn. A stage had been set up on a raised platform of rough planks. There was no covering to this stage except in so far as the sloping roofs of the surrounding pavilions jutted out above the courtyard. An orchestra of seven musicians was crowded into a corner with their instruments. The more important spectators were seated. The others stood behind them. The stage was lit up by means of hanging lanterns, some suspended from the eaves, some from tripods which raised them about two feet from the ground. High up, the uptilted roof corners stood out, inky black against a starry sky.

During the performance servants and attendants crossed and re-crossed the stage, now to relight a lantern that had gone out, now to replenish the cups of tea, which the actors sipped to moisten their throats.

The Chief Eunuch had the place of honour in the first row of spectators, but his thoughts were far away, and his expression never varied. Seated beside him was the local mandarin, whose pleasure at the unexpected treat was like that of a child. He listened with mouth agape; and his official necklace of wooden beads rolled about on his broad chest as he laughed and groaned in sympathy with the personages on the stage.

The players were conscious of the admiration they inspired, both by their acting and by the magnificence of their robes. Of these, the finest were worn by the actor who impersonated the Duke Chu-ke-liang. They were less gorgeous than the robes of the generals, but beautiful in their simplicity. Chu-ke-liang's coat was of wine-coloured silk, with the emblem of the three lines repeated many times in silver; his sleeves were light blue, embroidered with golden phoenixes. His hands were veiled in white silk, so that only the little fan was visible; the head-dress (of the Han dynasty) was a Doge's cap in black satin, blazing with jewels. Round his neck hung a long rope of ivory beads, interspersed with beads of jade.

A lantern caught fire near the entrance to the court-yard and the sudden flare drew a glance from the Chief Eunuch's half-closed eyes. In the light of those flames the gilded characters above the door stood out sharply: the *Yung*, the *Fu*, and the *Tien* that bid the traveller welcome. Liu-li-tè noticed them and smiled, for the sight appeared to him as a good omen. He felt comforted and encouraged. His doubts and fears faded away. On the morrow he would be in the presence, and his enemies would be taken by surprise. Some of them might learn the way of exile. . . .

Another drama followed the first without interruption or lowering of a curtain. It was called *Tien Nu San Huà*, 'The Heavenly Lady Sprinkling Flowers'.

168

A gigantic figure, with gilded face and black hair falling to his shoulders, represented the Buddha, enthroned among the sages. When he spoke, the ritual cacophony of drum and cymbal ceased for a moment, to recommence when other personages began to declaim. The Buddha's voice sounded unnaturally deep; it was meant to resemble thunder rumbling in a mountain pass. When he withdrew, his place was taken by the celestial lady. A man took the part, but so well was he made up that his appearance on the stage provoked a murmur of admiration. Young boys, dressed as girls, formed an escort, holding fans of blue ostrich feathers and wands of silver.

The local mandarin's delight became sheer ecstasy; his eyes started out of his head with excitement. Other spectators, blue-clad and clownish, crowded round agape. Their rustic senses were stupefied by the wonder of such costly scenes, enhanced as these were by the homely setting of a Chinese inn, in the homely atmosphere of a Chinese village.

Suddenly Liu-li-tè sprang to his feet with a sharp call for silence. The other spectators regarded him with astonishment. He shot a savage glance at the musicians, who had not immediately stopped playing. Slowly all sounds ceased, save the rustling of leaves in the poplars near the outer wall, as they swayed in the north wind. And that same wind brought another sound, which the Chief Eunuch, indifferent to the play, had heard before any one else: a sound of bells, like sleigh bells in a northern country.

Then all understood: a messenger from Jehol was on his way south. The mandarin made a sign, and a servant ran to saddle a horse, so that the imperial mail might continue on its way. But this time the messenger was not going to Peking. The sound of bells drew nearer and stopped at the door of the inn. A voice asked for the Tai-dien, for Liu-li-tè. Some one answered: 'He is here.'

The horseman dismounted and entered the courtyard.

He was a Mongol, and his face and clothes were covered with dust. On the front of his hat was a silver falcon with outstretched wings; round his waist a broad leather belt, to which were attached two rows of bells. The inn servants helped him to take off his belt. Underneath, and under the quilted robe, was another belt of yellow silk (the imperial yellow), light and dainty as a foulard.

The Chief Eunuch made a step forward, with an exclamation of impatience. He knew that among the folds of that yellow sash there was a letter for him: a private letter and not an Imperial Rescript, which would have had a whole delegation to accompany it.

Here the letter was, at last, in a long envelope striped with red lines. The Chief Eunuch opened it and began to read, while the people round him studied his face. In its way it was a fine face, though prematurely aged (as all eunuchs' faces are). One does not reach the supreme power in a great empire without possessing oneself some elements of greatness. Liu-li-tè's features revealed a subtle intellect, a dominating will.

This is what he read:

'Foreword: A Happy letter of joyful news to Liu-li-tè, Great Man. Open directly.

'Far away from your jewelled presence the days pass like years; but thinking of your great merit, and having at heart your supreme happiness, little by little I take comfort. In this season of the year, when the chrysanthemums open out in gorgeous colours and ten thousand fruits reach maturity, the painful desire of your presence urges me to cut a thumb-length of bamboo [*the paper on which he writes*] to express joyful sentiments of good augury.

'Writing briefly:

'At the news of your departure from the gates of Heaven, the miserable crowd of time-servers gave warning on high. The aspect of the Dragon became terrible. A decree has already been sent out, in which my Elder Brother [*The Chief Eunuch himself*] is exiled to the New Territory [*Turkestan*] to be a slave of the troops. But in extreme benevolence, and to give proof of the Dragon's infinite mercy, it is commanded that, before starting on his journey, my Elder Brother may manifest one desire, and the execution of his wish will be confirmed within a month, by a special Imperial Decree.

'This is only for your private information and to congratulate you on the magnanimity which comes from above. Rejoicing in your good health and continued prosperity, I limit myself to these few lines, to wish you continuous joy. Pardon me if I do not finish in accordance with the due forms, and if I omit half the ritual salutations.

'In great haste,

'THE LITTLE YOUNGER BROTHER
'(*Locus sigilli*)'

As Liu-li-tè ceased to read, he lifted his face, and for the second time that evening his glance fell on the three characters over the door of the hostelry. He gazed at them for a moment and, raising his hand, pointed them out to those who stood around him. Then he gave the order, his last order, which the Son of Heaven had promised to have carried out.

'To-morrow you will change the second character of that inscription. No longer *Fu*, but *Hen* shall be written there. And for ever to this house shall remain the name: Inn of Perpetual Misfortune. Before a month has passed an Imperial Decree will confirm my order.'

Such is the explanation of the ill-omened name.

wonder if Liu-li-tè, 'slave of the troops' in far-off Turkestan, found comfort in the memory of his last order and in the ill-fortune perpetuated in a name?

Before the door of that inn there passed, in 1860, the

tumult of the fleeing court, as it left Peking in confusion, while a foreign army advanced to burn the Summer Palace. There passed the bier of the Emperor Hsieng Feng, who died at Jehol while the empire threatened to crumble away amid the intrigues of the court. And finally, in 1911, lonely and sad as the *dernier des Abencer-rages*, passed the one general who was still faithful to the throne, and who, for that reason, was sent as Governor to Jehol, so that the empire might lose its only supporter and Young China might set up a Republic.

13   The Vase of the 'Famille Rose'

The porcelain of the Ta-yi kilns is light and yet strong.
It rings with a low jade note and is famed throughout
the city.
The fine white bowls surpass hoar frost and snow.
[*Verses of the poet Tu-mu, A.D. 803–52*]

Every afternoon, just after lunch (unless I give orders to
the contrary), my study is invaded by a group of curio-
dealers, who spread out their wares on the floor, or, if
the weather is warm, on the veranda outside, in the
hopes that I will be tempted to buy something.

Whatever the nature of these commodities, they are
done up in bundles of blue cotton, and all the ability of
the Chinese in making knots and in undoing them is
brought into play by the long brown fingers that open out
packages on arrival and do them up again on departure.
As happens with more important matters in China, even
the procedure of haggling over a piece of silk follows
certain ceremonial lines, so as to become a ritual. I
begin by saying that I do not want to buy anything, and
the dealers answer that all they wish is the pleasure of
showing me something very fine. If the 'something very
fine' is a length of damask, they hold it out with widespread arms the better to display the beauty of its tex-
ture and its sheen.

My own interest in curios is limited to silks, velvets, and
embroideries. Of these I have a small collection, to which
I add from time to time. I know little about porcelain and

173

jade, and have only a few specimens here and there about the house. The dealers who solicit my custom are mostly those who have their shops in the Street of the Silks. And they bring mandarin coats and rolls of brocade and cut velvets and embroidered cushions for leaning the elbow on as one sips one's tea.

Other dealers come and, though I rarely buy such things, offer snuff-bottles and cloisonné vases and plates which they swear are genuine K'ang-hsi or Ch'ien Lung.

Among these modest salesmen, who persist in bringing me curios that I don't want, is a fat little man with a round, oily face and a smile that seems to reveal an almost indecent pleasure in life. I buy something from him occasionally, out of a mistaken kindness, even though I feel that I would do better not to encourage him. He sells the most extraordinary rubbish. I have a specimen here before me on my writing-table, a *bibelot*, which he must have manufactured himself out of heterogeneous material. The base consists of a small Chinese cup of the commonest and cheapest kind, filled with brown clay in which is standing a fragment of what I imagine to have been the branch of a French chandelier, like a bunch of crystal grapes on a brass mount, except that a bunch of grapes hangs down, whereas this ornament now stands upright in the cup, and round its stem is a flat green surface made to imitate grass. This ridiculous combination is rather pretty, and the crystals catch the sunlight that streams on to my study table in the morning.

I paid one dollar (Mex.) for this ornament, and its owner assured me that in ceding it for that price he would lose money. If I am to believe what he says, he has never yet concluded a deal with me without losing on the transaction. Not knowing his honourable name, I now call him 'Lose Money', and he answers to this with perfect gravity.

Strange to say, poor old Lose Money was once mixed

up in a deal involving many thousands of pounds, and the knowledge of how great a commission he might have earned if he had played his cards with greater skill is another reason why I spend a dollar or two, now and then, on the *tung-shih* that he spreads out on my study carpet.

The story concerns a famous vase, known to collectors all the world over.

The firm of Reynolds, Whitehead & Co. of Liverpool, dealers in pictures, tapestries, porcelain, etc., which they export largely to the United States, had in their possession a Chinese vase of the type known as the *famille rose*. It was twenty-one inches high, not including the lid. Its colour was *rouge d'or*, decorated with four white medallions bearing designs representing the four seasons: the white prunus for winter, the peony for spring, the lotus flower for summer, and the chrysanthemum for autumn. The vase had a lid, which reproduced the same designs in miniature and was surmounted by a ball the colour of old gold. Its magnificent colouring, the nobility of its lines, the perfection of its glaze were such as to make of this vase a worthy expression of the Chinese sense of the beautiful, no less than a statue by Praxiteles expresses the artistic genius of Greece, or a painting by Leonardo that of Italy.

It is customary in China, and has been so from time immemorial, never to make a single vase of a given shape and design, but always two, and the pair is worth much more in proportion than two separate vases. The firm of Reynolds, Whitehead & Co. valued their vase at two thousand pounds sterling, but the pair would have been worth three times as much, and it would have been easier to find a museum or a collector willing to buy.

It was not improbable that the other vase of the pair existed and might be found in China. In Europe or in America its presence would have been known, no less than that of a picture by some old master. The person who had sold the single vase to the Liverpool firm (for four hundred guineas) was a Viennese dealer, who had bought it (for three hundred gulden) from a tea merchant, who had acquired it (for sixteen dollars and a bottle of gin) from a Russian soldier in Peking, at the time of the Boxer troubles in 1900. The second vase might still be found in the possession of some Chinese merchant or collector.

The great value of the vase possessed by Reynolds, Whitehead & Co. was proved also by the fact that an offer had come for it from the land of its origin. A young Chinese, looking like a student, had appeared one day at the offices of the firm in Liverpool and told a long story of how the vase had been stolen from his family. He urged that, in common justice, it should be given back, or at least sold to him for the price that had been given for it. Nobody paid much attention to him, and as the price was prohibitive, the young man went away and was not heard of again. It had been a mistake not to have asked his name and address. If it were really true that the vase had been stolen from his family he might have given some clue to the whereabouts of its fellow.

From the moment when the vase of the *famille rose* was first shown in the shop of the Liverpool firm and thus began to be known to connoisseurs in Chinese art, many dealers with agents in China and Japan had considered the possibility of finding the companion. But all inquiries proved fruitless.

It was in 1912 that Reynolds, Whitehead & Co. decided to send a special agent of their own to institute a systematic search for the companion vase in China and also in Japan (where most of the best Chinese porcelain finds its way). The cost of the expedition was to be defrayed, even if its special object was not attained, by the profit on the sale of other curios that might be acquired by the agent during his journey.

The man chosen for this interesting mission was Paul Ritter, a naturalized Englishman. His name, savouring of chivalry, and the fact that his family came originally from the country of Wolfram von Eschenbach, accentuated in him that spirit of romance which is found sometimes in collectors of antiques and more rarely in dealers. The idea of making a journey to the Far East to seek a vase whose very existence was uncertain appealed to Paul Ritter's imagination like a new quest for the Holy Grail. He was accompanied by his brother, a youth of eighteen, called Rudolph, who took no interest in curios, but had joined the expedition for reasons of his own. These might be indicated by the phrase *cherchez la femme*, though as a matter of fact the idea was not to seek for the lady, whose whereabouts were much advertised, but rather to avoid her.

The brothers Ritter embarked at Genoa, and after an uneventful journey arrived in Hong-Kong and set to work to scour the principal towns of China for valuable porcelain. They began with Canton and ended with Peking. The elder brother got in touch with local dealers, examined their wares, not infrequently bought them, and everywhere offered a tempting reward to any one who could find him a *famille rose* jar, with cover, richly decorated with panel pictures of flowers on a *rouge d'or* background. Many jars were brought to him that seemed to answer this description. None proved to be the companion of the vase in Liverpool.

During their stay in Peking, the two brothers came to call on me. They brought an introduction from a mutual friend in London, and Paul Ritter professed a desire to see my collection of silks. I asked them to lunch, and after lunch we allowed the usual dealers to come in and show their wares. Paul Ritter bought a series of panels from a merchant called Little Li with whom I have had many dealings, and Rudolph a cheap jade ring from my old friend Lose Money.

A few days later Paul Ritter started for Japan. His brother remained in Peking.

About ten days after our lunch, I was walking up Legation Street, in the Diplomatic Quarter, when a group of foreigners passed me in rickshaws. I had time to notice two very pretty girls among them. Then one of the rickshaws stopped and Rudolph Ritter jumped out, waving his hand to his friends as a sign not to wait for him. He hailed me with considerable cordiality and said that I was just the man he most wanted to see. Apparently he wished to consult me about something.

He began by asking if I remembered the oily little Chinese curio-dealer who had sold him a jade ring at my house.

'I suppose you mean Lose Money,' I answered.

'Is that what you call him? I should not have thought he had much money to lose. Anyway he came to see me this morning at the hotel.'

'What rubbish does he want to pawn off on you now?'

'Nothing less than the vase that my brother is looking for.'

'I am sure that Lose Money does not possess anything one quarter so valuable.'

'He says that he knows where it is and can get it for me.'

'And what did you say?'

'I told him to wait till my brother comes back from Japan. I know nothing about Chinese porcelain and care less.'

'And what then?'

'Lose Money does not want to wait, and what he proposes is so very shady, that I was rather short with him and ended by telling him to go to the devil.'

I waited for further explanations.

'That man is a swindler, I should say,' Rudolph continued. 'But he seems to know all about me and my brother and why we are here and where we are going. He even knew that I am starting for Mukden to-morrow night, though we only decided on the trip yesterday.'

'We? Is your brother back already?'

'Oh, dear, no. I am going to join him in Japan, and on the way I will step off at Mukden with some friends who

178

are here with me in the hotel. You saw them just now: those people who were in the rickshaws.'

'I congratulate you. One at least was very pretty, possibly two, though I had no time to make certain.'

'The pretty one is Pearl. She is a peach. And Nelly is an attractive little thing too.'

'An apricot, shall we say?'

'A very good name for her.'

'And Lose Money is aware of your proclivities?'

'He knows, at all events, that we are starting for Mukden together, and he offers to bring me the famous vase to some station called Tang-shan. He says he will hand it over to me when the train stops there at five in the morning. He asks two thousand dollars for it.'

'Surely it is worth more than that?'

'Of course it is. That is what makes me think he means to steal it.'

'And what do you propose to do?'

'I don't know. That is what I wanted to see you about.'

'What does Lose Money say, exactly?'

'He tells the most ridiculous story. He says that the vase belongs to an old Chinese mandarin, who does not want to sell. But the mandarin is very ill, at death's door, in fact. His sons and daughters and nephews and nieces will be quite willing to sell. Indeed they propose to do so, to pay for the old man's funeral.'

'I don't believe a word of it.'

'Neither do I. But Lose Money swears that he will be at the station with the vase and beseeches me not to lose the opportunity of buying it.'

'Some Chinese merchants are reliable. You can trust them implicitly. But Lose Money is not of their number. I advise you to be careful.'

'That is what I feel about it. Anyway I must be getting on. I will let you know if I really do get the famous vase.'

Rudolph took leave of me and got into the rickshaw again. As I continued on my way alone, I thought to myself that it might be with him as with the youngest brother in some fairy tales; he might marry the King's daughter and find the magic ring or whatever it was that the other members of his family had set out to do.

But it was odd to think of poor old Lose Money being mixed up in such important transactions.

I did not really expect to hear anything more about the brothers Ritter and their search. And since Rudolph had told me that he was going to Japan to join Paul there, I thought it unlikely that I should see them again.

But a fortnight after meeting Rudolph in Legation Street, I received a letter of many typewritten pages from his brother. It was dated from Yokohama and told me a long story of certain happenings which occurred during Rudolph's journey north. I prefer to give this story in my own words, for the narrative, as contained in Paul's letter, was supplemented at a later date by details told me by Rudolph himself.

The day after he had seen me, Rudolph took the evening train for Mukden. The same train conveyed the two American girls and their parents, who were leaving for Europe via Siberia on a tour of pleasure and instruction. It was really to enjoy the company of the Peach and the Apricot that Rudolph chose to travel to Japan by way of Manchuria and Korea and did not avail himself of the boat which leaves once a week for Kobe, from Tientsin. According to the time-table, the train ought to have reached Tang-shan at a quarter to five a.m. Rudolph had not been able to sleep for the heat, although he had a compartment to himself. At each stop, from three o'clock onwards, he would pull up the window screen and endeavour to make out the name of the place by the uncertain light of the station lamps. When the train reached Tang-shan, the dawn was breaking, but although Rudolph scanned the platform he saw no signs of Lose Money and the promised vase. 'It would seem,' he said to himself, 'as if the old mandarin's family were not yet in need of money for a funeral.'

Giving up all idea of sleep, Rudolph began to dress.

About an hour later, the train stopped again at a small station called Chang-li, and Rudolph stepped out on to the platform, to get a breath of morning air. The first person he saw, in the midst of a group of Chinamen carrying baskets of fruit, was Lose Money. He too had a basket, and seeing Rudolph, he ran up to him.

'Glapes', he exclaimed. 'Beautiful glapes! Two dolla' basket; only two dolla'. Velly cheap!'

They were the same words with which the other fruit-sellers on the platform accosted the few foreigners whose heads appeared at the windows of the train. Chang-li is a little town renowned for its fruit, and many sales take place at the railway station. As a rule, the price is agreed upon and the transfer effected only when the train is actually moving off.

Lose Money now presented himself in the guise of a fruit-seller, but he made a sign to the astonished Rudolph, to show that there was something behind the offer of a basket of grapes. And he added in a whisper:

'Vase inisy. Vase under glapes. Master makee look-see wantchee glape. Pay my two dolla'. Master takee inisy calliage, catchee vase. Pay my two thousan' dolla'.'

This proposal was so unexpected that Rudolph did not know what to say. He looked at the basket, that appeared to be full of grapes. But he noticed that the shape and size were such that a vase might well be hidden inside. He therefore made a pretence of examining the fruit. Lifting out a bunch of grapes, he probed with his fingers. They came in contact with a smooth, hard surface. The basket really did contain a vase. Rudolph had not got so large a sum as two thousand dollars with him. Nor was he an expert in *objets d'art*. It did not matter very much to him whether the vase hidden under the grapes was really that which Reynolds, Whitehead & Co. were seeking. But his gambling instincts were aroused by Lose Money's strange proposal. It was a question of staking a certain sum, great or small, on the chance that in that basket, under those grapes, there might be an object of great value. That the dealer who proposed the bargain was a cheat and a thief, there could be little doubt; but it was not clear whether in that moment he was trying to hoodwink a possible buyer, or whether he found himself obliged by circumstances to dispose of his wares in a clandestine manner and therefore at an absurdly low price.

It was also possible that the comedy of the fruit-basket offered at a station, between the arrival and the departure of a train, was staged with the object of preventing any careful examination of the vase. Rudolph had no time to reason out the matter, but he grasped the situation as a whole and decided on the amount of his offer, as a roulette-player decides during the turn of a wheel, the amount of his stake.

'Two dollars is too much', he said, as if he were speaking of the grapes. 'I will give you one dollar if you like.' So saying, he extracted from his pocket-book a hundred-dollar note, folded and refolded it until it could be covered by one silver dollar, and placing it under the coin which he offered for the grapes, he held them both out to Lose Money. The latter drew back nonplussed. He understood that Rudolph intended to bargain for the vase, while seeming only to want the grapes. But on his part he did not know how to haggle about the price without mentioning the larger sum. Time was short. In his embarrassment, Lose Money began to bring down his price at a precipitous rate. 'Master', he said, 'two dolla' velly little for these beautiful glapes', and then in an undertone: 'One thousan' dolla', Master. Only one thousan'. Big blother, he offer ten thousan'.'

'Nothing doing,' said Rudolph with a shrug, and pocketing his money he strolled off towards the other fruit-sellers and began to bargain with one of them for a basket of pears. By this time, Lose Money's smile no longer concealed his growing anxiety. This mad fool of a foreign devil hardly seemed to be taking his offer seriously. In a few minutes the train would start. There was barely time for those preliminary skirmishes in the long-drawn battle, which should precede every business transaction between well-mannered people. Meanwhile Rudolph, with another example of a promptitude that was contrary to all custom, had concluded the purchase of the pears and was walking along the platform, looking for his carriage window in order to put the basket in the train. He seemed to have forgotten about the grapes, the China vase and their owner.

Lose Money approached him once more, repeating his double offer, and again Rudolph, with an air of complete indifference, replied, 'I will give you one dollar, but no more.' And again he held out the silver piece with the hundred-dollar note beneath it, half hidden, but visible to Lose Money, who drew back protesting. Rudolph, having seemingly given up all idea of further bargaining, returned to his compartment. On the platform at the end of the sleeping-carriage, he met one of the two American girls (it was Nelly, 'the Apricot') looking fresh and pretty in spite of the night in a hot train. As Rudolph greeted her, Lose Money, resting his basket of grapes on the step of the car platform, held it with one hand, while he kept on repeating: 'Two dolla', Master. Only two dolla'. Velly cheap.'

But Rudolph paid no attention.

A whistle sounded; harsh voices shouted; the few passengers who had been walking on the platform hurried into the train again.

'Two dolla', Master. Only two dolla'. Velly cheap!'

A creaking of buffers and steel couplings, a puff from the engine, and the train began to move. On the steps of the carriage next to the one where Rudolph and the Apricot were standing, another fruit-seller had put down his basket of apples and was still bargaining with a Japanese officer. The same scene was being enacted at the end of almost every carriage.

'What lovely grapes!' exclaimed the girl to Rudolph

while Lose Money continued to offer his wares, though by now he was almost obliged to run.

'Do you want them?'

'I should like them. But two dollars is too much for that basket.'

Rudolph assumed an air of gallantry. 'For once in a way,' he said. 'I might be able to afford it.' Then, turning to Lose Money, who was showing signs of being unable to keep up much longer, he called:

'Here you are. You have earned your two dollars all right.'

At the same moment, Rudolph seized the basket – the train was beginning to move quickly – and he dropped two silver dollars into Lose Money's hand. He had acted on an impulse, and it was with real amazement that he found himself the possessor of the basket and all it contained for the small amount of two dollars.

The Apricot talked on as if nothing unusual had happened.

'Did you see the face of that Chinese, when you took the grapes?' she asked. 'He looked just rattled. Perhaps he never expected to get the price he asked.'

'Very likely,' said Rudolph.

'And now that you have bought the grapes, aren't you going to offer me any?'

'Not yet. First I must get them washed. They tell me it is dangerous to eat fruit in China just as you buy it. I will wash them myself, so as to be quite sure.'

Rudolph went to his compartment, shut himself in and proceeded to take the grapes out of the basket.

Buried under the bunches was a large vase, which in shape was like the one sought for by Reynolds, Whitehead and Co., but of an entirely different colour. The vase which Rudolph had bought in such a peculiar and unexpected manner was of a nondescript shade, something between light yellow and grey. It had panels, but the flowers therein were only outlined in red, without detail or finish.

Rudolph felt half inclined to throw the thing out of the window. But he refrained, thinking that, after all, two dollars was not a large sum to have paid for it. He washed the grapes that were included in the bargain, and returned to console himself with the Apricot.

Such is the story – more or less – that Rudolph told his brother when they met again in Japan. In writing to me, Paul drew the following conclusions:

'All this is strange and puzzling enough. But there is an added circumstance that escaped my brother Rudolph and makes me suspect that there is really some mystery hidden under the absurd adventure in the train. The vase bought at Chang-li in a basket of grapes is the exact replica of the vase that I am seeking, except for the colour. The lines are identical, the measurements correspond, even the design of flowers inside the panels is the same. But the vase is colourless; a yellowish grey that is the tinge of the untinted clay, and the flowers are merely traced in red as a painter might trace the lines of a picture in charcoal, before beginning to paint. It looks as if this vase had been through the furnace before the colours were laid on.

'What does it all mean? Can you explain? You know China and the Chinese better than I do. Perhaps you can enlighten me.'

My first impulse, on receiving Paul Ritter's letter, was to send for Lose Money and ask him for an explanation. But Lose Money was not to be found in Peking. Which made me suspect that he had a bad conscience.

The locality first mentioned in Lose Money's proposal to Rudolph Ritter was Tang-shan. And this gave me an idea. I had a friend there, who knew China and the Chinese much better than I did. This was the Reverend Jacob Carlin.

He was one of the oldest foreign residents in the

185

country, having arrived in Shanghai on a tea-clipper some time about the middle of the last century. He was also known as the husband of the ugliest woman between the 15th and the 125th degrees of longitude. Poor Carlin's marriage was a standing joke among Old China hands.

When he first settled in China women were rarer among the foreign community than they are now. The Reverend Jacob had need of a teacher for a girls' school of Chinese converts, but as soon as they arrived to take up their duties, some one would marry them, and the Chinese converts would be without a teacher once more.

Tired of acting as a matrimonial agent, the Reverend Jacob wrote home, beseeching the headquarters of his mission to send out a young woman whose appearance might reasonably justify the assumption that marriage, in her case, was out of the question. Officials at home did their best. The person selected would never have found a husband, even in China, if the Reverend Jacob, a year after her arrival, had not married her himself.

I felt that if any one could explain the mystery of the Chang-li vase it would be old Carlin, who lived in that district. So I wrote to him, enclosing Paul Ritter's letter to me. His answer, which reached me less than a week later, was satisfactory inasmuch as it told me that the vase which Paul Ritter had been seeking for actually existed, though it might not be for sale. This is what he wrote:

'I thank you for your kind remembrance of me and I shall be most happy if I can be of use in the matter of the vase. If the search thereof should procure me the pleasure of seeing you again, I shall be grateful to the worldly vanity that sets so high a value upon such things.

'The information contained in Mr. Ritter's letter made it easy for me to trace the vase itself. But the discovery of its whereabouts does not imply the possibility of acquiring it. The little dealer whom you call

"Lose Money" was not wholly untruthful: the vase will not come into the market until after the death of the present owner. The description of the Chang-li vase revealed to me the identity of the possessor of that other, of which the Chang-li one is only a colourless reproduction. I do not know if it would be possible to deceive so great an expert as Mr. Paul Ritter with an exact copy of an antique vase, but it is obvious that no one, *unless he were blind*, could possibly be imposed upon by a vase of a different colour to the one he seeks. Now it happens that, at Luan-chow (a town on the railway line, not far from here) there lives an old mandarin, a Manchu and a friend of mine, who possesses a collection of ancient porcelain, not a large collection, but containing – so I am told – pieces of great value. And for the past twenty years the old man has been blind. On receiving your letter and enclosure, I immediately repaired to Luan-chow, to inquire whether the *famille rose* vase belonged to my friend and to find out whether he would sell it and for what price. The vase is there. I saw it myself, and though I am no judge of porcelain it struck me as being a fine work of art. But for the moment there can be no question of it being sold.

'My friend's name is Su, better known as "Su of the Bricks". Many years ago, when he held office, during the Empress Tzu Hsi's second regency, there occurred a painful episode connected with the distribution of rice to the Manchu Banners. Old Su's cheating in the matter of Army contracts was so notorious that one fine day the soldiers on guard at the gates of the Winter Palace, disgusted with the bad rice he had dealt out to them, laid wait in an outer courtyard and greeted his palanquin with a discharge of bricks. A wound on the head, received on this occasion, was the original cause of his blindness.

'Now that he lives in retirement, old Su's financial affairs are entrusted to a grandson whose name is, or rather was, Pu-we-chi. Since he has been in Europe, to complete his education, this young man has adopted a western name of his own invention and possesses visiting cards on which is printed the legend: *Mr. C. Rembrandt Pu.*

'It was to him that I revealed Mr. Ritter's wish to buy the vase, and he at once begged me to say nothing to his grandfather. Old Su of the Bricks is verging on his second childhood and the idea that he might be deprived of his treasures would be very disturbing to him. Although he no longer sees his vases, they are still his greatest joy. From time to time he examines them, touching them lovingly with the tips of his fingers. Nothing would induce him to forgo this pleasure. The distribution of mouldy rice to the Eight Banners, during many years, has brought him considerable wealth. No sum that Mr. Ritter might be disposed to offer would compensate him for the loss of even a single specimen.

'But Mr. Ritter might come to some arrangement with the grandson, for purchasing the vase after the death of old Su of the Bricks. It is not likely that he will live much longer. He is a very old man. He and I are of the same age. . . .

'As for the enigma of the Chang-li vase, I can shed no light on the subject. I spoke to C. Rembrandt Pu about it, but he knows nothing, or more probably he will not say.

'If Mr. Ritter thinks it worth while to come back from Japan and to step off at Luan-chow, to see old Su's collection, I am sure the latter would be only too happy to show it. But any proposal to buy should be made only to the grandson. Although young Rembrandt Pu speaks fluent English, it might be well if I were to come too. Could we not all meet, some day soon, at Luan-chow?

'Yours very sincerely,

'JACOB CARLIN'

Naturally, old Carlin's proposal was welcomed by Paul Ritter, and towards the end of the month we all met, as suggested, at Luan-chow. I joined the party because by that time I too was genuinely interested in the famous vase, and also because I did not think it fair to poor Carlin to give him so much trouble for the sake of my friends and not to join him and them in the expedition that he so kindly organized.

Luan-chow is a small town on the right bank of the Hoan-ho river, not far from its mouth. I and the brothers Ritter arrived there about half-past three on a fine afternoon and found the Reverend Jacob on the station platform with one of his granddaughters, a girl of eighteen. She had accompanied him to see that he did not overtire himself and to help him in any little difficulty that the journey might involve. There was no trace, in this girl, of her grandmother's well-known ugliness. Rudolph Ritter, who had been looking bored, brightened up considerably at the prospect of feminine society. For him the opposite sex offered the principal interest in life, and he pursued his own hobby with no less enthusiasm than his brother showed in searching for old porcelain.

We were taken to Mr. Su's house in chairs, up a steep hill path. It was a fine villa in Chinese style, overlooking town and river. Our host was led as far as the threshold of the principal pavilion to meet us, his arms resting on the shoulders of two attendants. He was a fine-looking old man, tall and dignified, with a white beard, which though scanty, as all Chinese beards are, added to his patriarchal appearance. But a habit of constant expectoration, over which his blindness prevented his exercising a complete control, rendered his vicinity dangerous.

In spite of this failing, the old mandarin, robed in silk and sables, and wearing the insignia of his official rank, with his descendants and retainers grouped around him, gave an impression of gracious stateliness, reminiscent of a historic past.

Among the members of the family was a youth, who appeared to be about twenty years old. He differed from the others by having his hair cut in Western fashion with a parting at the side. Like many Chinese men, he was probably older than he looked. This was the grandson, C. Rembrandt Pu. Although he no longer boasted a pigtail, he was dressed in a Chinese coat of fine brocade.

The old man received us with all the formality prescribed by an ancient ceremonial: bows, smiles, compliments, questions intended to show a kindly interest in the health and prosperity of the brothers Ritter, of myself, of the Reverend Jacob and his granddaughter, not forgetting our relations and the states to which we belonged. We sat in a semi-circle in the central hall of the house, while all around stood domestic servants redolent of garlic, not to mention a crowd of small children, none of whom appeared familiar with the uses of a pocket handkerchief.

At least one hour passed in conversation that had no bearing on the object of our visit. Such are the exigencies of Chinese etiquette. If a Chinese has a fish-bone in his throat and goes to a doctor to have it taken out, he will not fail – unless his breath does – to begin the conversation on topics that have nothing to do with his trouble.

At last came the moment when Mr. Su gave orders to fetch his treasures, to show to the foreign collector. Evening was drawing in, and the servants brought in kerosene lamps of modern manufacture, that struck an outlandish note in the old Chinese harmony. Then the vases were carried in one at a time and placed upon a table near Mr. Su. They were encased in wooden boxes, closed by sliding panels on which were gummed strips of red silk with Chinese characters, describing the article within. Each vase rested in a niche that moulded its outline, thus diminishing the risk of breakage. As the sliding panel was removed, the effect was that of a jewel-case being opened. The glazes shone with an almost phosphorescent light. Mr. Su, not being able to enjoy the sight of his treasures, yet bent over them with sensuous adoration, stroking them with his fingers, but never lifting one from its case. He might have been bending over a cradle. His touch was a caress.

Of every kind, there was a pair. Two vases of the *famille noire*, two of the five colours, two of the blue of K'ang-hsi, and so on. Some of the older vases had no painted design; they were monochrome, of a faint olive green. One vase stood bereaved of its mate: a vase of the *famille rose*, the colour of rose petals powdered with gold. Four white medallions represented the seasons (the prunus, the peony, the lotus and the chrysanthemum). The lid reproduced the same designs in miniature and was surmounted by a ball the colour of old gold.

I looked at Paul Ritter. He stood like one entranced. The supreme moment of his quest had come. The Holy Grail was found!

Even Rudolph seemed impressed. And the Reverend Jacob, while acting as interpreter, did his best, for the sake of good manners, to hide his own indifference to such mundane vanities.

C. Rembrandt Pu came up to Paul Ritter and offered him a magnifying-glass. 'It is worth while,' he said in perfect English, 'to examine some of these vases in detail. This pair of the *famille noire* is the most valuable of the collection. Look how the flowers are painted. One can almost smell them.'

Paul Ritter took one of the two vases nearer to the lamp to see it better. He and the young Chinaman were standing close to me and at a little distance from our host. C. Rembrandt Pu spoke in a low voice to Paul.

'I must thank you,' he said, 'for not having expressed any desire to buy. My grandfather would have been very upset. You can see how infatuated he is with his treasures.'

'He has every reason to be!' exclaimed Paul.

191

It is not advisable to show enthusiasm for an object that one wishes to buy, at least not before the price is settled. But the older Ritter's prudence was overcome by the passion of a connoisseur. In many cases there may be doubt as to the genuineness of a vase said to be antique. But the wonderful pair of the *famille noire* bore every stamp of authenticity. We stood before the masterpiece.

'I hope,' said Paul, 'that you will give me an option, should this collection ever come on the market.'

'I think there would be no difficulty', replied C. Rembrandt Pu.

'Would you be willing to sign an agreement to that effect?' asked Paul.

'I am sorry, but that would not be possible. None of us could enter into an agreement in the name of the family without my grandfather's consent. And it would be unkind to speak to him about it. But there is one thing that we can do. I wonder if you possess such a thing as a Chinese seal?'

'A Chinese seal? No. What use would that be?'

'In China, as you know, a personal seal corresponds to a signature. It occurred to me that your seal, placed on the boxes that contain these vases, might be taken as the assertion of a claim for the future. But perhaps we can manage, even without a seal.'

So saying, he took out of his pocket a small metal box. Inside was an ivory seal, engraven with Chinese characters, and an ink-pad.

'This is my seal,' he said, in answer to a question of Paul's. 'It used to be the fashion to take impressions in a vermilion paste made of cinnabar. But nowadays, we all find it more practical to use an ink-pad, as you do in Europe.'

'But what do you wish *me* to do with it?'

'You might use this ink-pad to imprint your finger prints on the surface of the vases you wish to buy. Your thumb would be enough. It may seem illogical, but to the

192

Chinese mind such an imprint might well appear a claim to possession. It would also have the advantage of rendering any substitution impossible, supposing that the vases, when sent to your firm, should pass through the hands of an agent or intermediary.'

Paul raised some small objection: 'Isn't it possible,' he said, 'that the finger prints might disappear when the vases are washed or dusted?'

C. Rembrandt Pu smiled. 'You need have no fear,' he said. 'My grandfather will allow no one to touch his vases, and he would be afraid to handle them himself.'

Some hours later, we started down the hill towards the station, to catch the south-bound Mukden express, which stopped at Luan-chow shortly before midnight. This time, for some reason, chairs were not available. But the path went downhill. Although the moon was full, servants preceded us, carrying lanterns. Paul Ritter was jubilant. He was sure now that in time he would obtain the famous vase of the *famille rose* and others no less desirable and precious. He walked on ahead, talking to C. Rembrandt Pu, who told of his own studies in Europe, of acquaintances he had made, and of his present hopes to bring a breath of modern civilization into his native town of Luan-chow.

Rudolph Ritter appeared no less satisfied than his brother with the evening and his surroundings. While the others had been busy over porcelain, he had started an animated flirtation with old Carlin's granddaughter. On leaving the house, he offered her his arm down the path, which was steep and stony. Far more than his granddaughter the old Pastor needed a friendly arm to help him on his way. I offered him mine, which he accepted gratefully. The young love-birds walked in front of us, talking and laughing. Their combined ages did not make fifty years, and it was a moonlight night.

Old Carlin leant on my arm and on his stick, and paused every now and then to see if the station lamps seemed any nearer. A light breeze, passing over the little town, brought to our ears a confusion of nocturnal sounds. On a boat by the river bank some one was playing a stringed instrument with musical intent. Dogs barked at the moon. A night watchman went his rounds, beating a drum to warn off evil spirits of this world or the next.

Old Su of the Bricks died in February 1913, and the preliminary negotiations for the purchase of his collection of porcelain were conducted by C. Rembrandt Pu, representing the heirs of the deceased, and the Reverend Jacob Carlin, representing Paul Ritter and his firm. The difficulties attending the sale of the collection did not cease on the death of the old mandarin. The heirs announced that for the moment they would sell only the *famille rose* vase, which had no pair. They would discuss the sale of the other vases at some future date. Moreover they made it a condition of immediate sale of the *famille rose* vase that the entire price should be paid over at once, before delivery. On the other hand, the price itself was not exorbitant: eight thousand dollars Mex. The firm of Reynolds, Whitehead & Co. would have been willing to pay much more.

The vase was sent off in its own box, but with strips of paper gummed over the outside and inside, to augment the resistance of the porcelain. The box was then placed among great wads of cotton wool, inside a small barrel, reinforced with iron and india-rubber bands. By request of C. Rembrandt Pu, a letter to Paul Ritter was placed inside the barrel, so that he might receive it at the same time as the vase.

A month or two later, Rudolph Ritter was kind enough to write to me a letter announcing his own engagement to a young lady who, so he said, was pretty and attractive and blessed with a considerable fortune of her own.

'So you see I am much to be congratulated. I am afraid that I cannot say the same of Paul. Would you believe it? His precious vase turned out to be a fake, after all! And brother Paul got left, just like Lose Money did on the station platform at Chang-li. I am glad I never took much interest in old china.'

That was all. No explanation, no other comment. Rudolph's letter left me utterly puzzled. How *could* those vases be fakes?

There was only one person in China who might solve the riddle: old Carlin, at Tang-shan. I wrote to him.

An answer came back in due course, not from Carlin himself but from his granddaughter: the one who had accompanied us to Kuan-chow. She told me that her grandfather had been much distressed to hear that the vase, forwarded to England, was not a genuine piece. Indeed he was so upset that he had taken to his bed. On the other hand, C. Rembrandt Pu was pleased with himself, and boasted that he 'had got a bit of his own back.'

A full explanation was contained in the letter from C. Rembrandt Pu to Paul Ritter: the letter which was enclosed with the vase, when it was dispatched to Liverpool. (I wish Rudolph had told me something about the scene when the barrel was opened!) Later on, a copy of this letter was sent, on request, to poor Carlin, and he kindly forwarded it to me. It is rather a remarkable document.

To Paul Ritter, Esq.,
   c/o Reynolds, Whitehead & Co.,
     Liverpool

LUAN-CHOW, July 16th, 1913

'DEAR MR. RITTER,

'The vase which will reach you together with this letter, although it bears your finger-print, is not the pair to the one in possession of your firm. It is an imitation that I had made in the Imperial German

Factory at Kadinen, when Messrs. Reynolds, Whitehead & Co. refused, not very courteously, to let me buy back the vase which had been stolen from our house in Peking in 1900. In case this refusal should have slipped the firm's memory, let me remind them of my visit to Liverpool (at that time I was a student at the London University) in August 1905. The vase which you have sought so long exists no more. It was broken into hundreds of pieces during the looting of the Tartar City. The fragments served as a model for the vase made in Germany six years later. It was a most successful imitation, but could hardly have deceived an expert like yourself, had not our refusal to sell at once and the fact that you saw it among others of undoubted authenticity put you off your guard, so that you took precautions to avoid deception in the future, but omitted to make sure that there was no deception when you first saw the vase.

'I must have seemed a simple and perhaps even a ridiculous young man, when I endeavoured to persuade the partners in Reynolds, Whitehead & Co. to let me have back our vase.

'I trust you will not take it to heart if you have lost in this little return match, and if the expert representative of Reynolds, Whitehead & Co. should appear for once no less simple than I did in 1905. On the bottom of the vase that I am sending you there is the seal of Yung Chen (and your thumb mark), but on the inside you will find the imperial crown surmounting a *W*, thus showing quite clearly that it is an imitation.

'The price you have paid for this imitation will just cover the cost of my studies in Europe and the bill from the porcelain works at Kadinen. You cannot bring an action against us, for we gave you no guarantee of authenticity, nor did you ask for one. With regard to the other vases of my grandfather's collection, we shall be happy to sell them to you with all due guarantees and for the price that is usual for such works of art. Your option still holds good.

'I have only to add that the German vase was a great joy to my grandfather, who thought I had succeeded in buying back the original that had been stolen from him in 1900. A former attempt at an imitation was that colourless vase, which was also stolen from our house and then sold to your brother for two dollars (a stupid attempt at fraud, which served, however, to bring you to Luan-chow). It was made in China before my journey to Europe, but did not deceive my grandfather, who could distinguish the flowery patterns by touch alone.

'That is all.

'I await your decision in the matter of the remaining vases and hope you will still believe me,

'Yours sincerely,

'C. REMBRANDT PU'

I have pondered over the episode of the vase de la famille rose, and asked myself if the tale does not inculcate some practical lesson. But the only moral I can discover is that in their different pursuits – old china and young women – it was the younger of the two brothers who was the more fortunate. For after much philandering he has succeeded in winning the bride of his choice.

14   Voices in the Desert

Kuniang has many Chinese friends, with whom she gets
on better than with some Europeans and Americans.
One of her friends was Yur, the daughter of Mr. Su,
comprador of the Russian Bank in Peking. In Chinese
Yur is the diminutive of Yu, which means 'moon'.
'Comprador' is a local term of Portuguese origin, meaning 'a Chinese agent or representative'; there is one
attached to every foreign bank or firm. I don't suppose I
would ever have made friends with 'The Little Moon'
had it not been for her intimacy with Kuniang, but I
know Mr. Su fairly well. He is an important person in
financial circles, very wealthy and possessing a certain
amount of Western culture. He belongs to the new class
of Chinese business men, with modern ideas and cosmopolitan habits (or, at least, that is the impression he first
gave me). He has published a series of articles on the
currency question, and plays a good game of bridge.

Despite his knowledge of the West, Mr. Su has not
abandoned his national dress and manner of living. His
office at the bank is furnished in foreign style, but his
house in the Tartar City (not far from the Shuang Liè
Ssè) is still typically Chinese, and, except that they own
a motor-car, use the telephone and mix freely with
foreigners, he and his family live – much as their
fore-fathers did. I rather admire Mr. Su for this
conservatism.

Although established in Peking with his family, Mr. Su
came originally from Canton and he brought with him an

excellent Cantonese cook. In the first years after his arrival here he gave frequent dinners, to which he was sometimes kind enough to ask me. I accepted his invitations with pleasure, for at Mr. Su's house one could enjoy Chinese cooking at its best. It was at one of these dinners that I first met his daughter. This fact shows how very advanced (for his day) were Mr. Su's views. In an old-styled Chinese family, the most secluded part of the house is reserved for budding womanhood, and young daughters are relegated to special pavilions with appropriate names, such as The Court of Spring Flowering, The Springtime Bower, etc.

On my first meeting with Yur, I opened the conversation with the usual remarks concerning the 'pretty flowers', with which the room (not the table) was decorated. But when she asked after Kuniang, I suddenly recalled having seen her more than once passing through the courtyards of my own house. She and Kuniang also met, so I gathered, in the house of the Russian family. As Mr. Su was in the Russian Bank, many of his foreign friends belong to the Russian colony in Peking. As the evening wore on, my talk with Yur became pleasant enough, and we soon abandoned those formal banalities that are proper to the intercourse between foreign men and Chinese women. She was quite amusing on the subject of the Russian family. To her Chinese eyes they must have seemed utter barbarians.

Next day I told Kuniang that I had sat next to her friend at dinner. And Kuniang gave me an entirely unexpected piece of information about her.

'Do you know, Fédor has some idea of writing a scenario for a film and putting Yur into it as principal lady!'

'She never told me that! Yur as a film star! Well, she is pretty enough, I must say. What role would she have to take?'

'Fédor thinks she could take the part of Cocachin, the princess, in a film on Marco Polo.'

'I don't seem to remember any love-story in Marco Polo's travels.'

'Perhaps not. But you must have a love-story in a film, to make it a success. And Marco Polo would fall in love with Yur . . . I mean Cocachin.'

'Who was Cocachin, anyway?'

'Fédor says she was the Chinese princess, who was sent to Persia to marry the king there. The two uncles of Marco Polo and Marco himself were sent with her as an escort. The uncles were old, so that was all right. But Marco Polo was only thirty-two, and it would be quite natural if, on the long sea-journey, he and Cocachin were to fall in love.'

'Like Tristan and Iseult. That is not unlikely, if Cocachin were as pretty as Yur. What happens in Fédor's scenario?'

'Marco Polo wants to leave the ship and settle down with Cocachin on an island in the East Indies, and live there with her and be happy ever after. The uncles pretend to agree, but at the wedding dinner they give Marco a cup of wine drugged with opium. When he is asleep, they take him on board again and set sail.'

'Leaving Cocachin, like Ariadne, on the island?'

'No. They take her along, but on another ship.'

'Fédor seems to possess imagination, but I doubt if his scenario would be accepted at Hollywood, or that Yur would get taken on as a leading lady. What does Mr. Su think of it all?'

'He is rather puzzled. On the one hand, he would like Yur to shine in Western society. On the other, he will not admit of her having even a fictitious love-affair that does not lead to an immediate marriage. I don't think that Fédor will bring it off.'

'Hasn't he given you a part in the story?'

'Rather! I'm to be the Venetian girl that Marco Polo marries when he gets home.'

'How dull, if he loves some one else! Has Fédor any idea who should take the part of Marco Polo?'

Kuniang smiled demurely as she answered:

'He would have to leave that to the producer. But he says that his own idea would be somebody who looked like you!'

This conversation naturally increased my interest in Yur. And the next time I met her, coming into the Shuang Liè Ssè to see Kuniang, I stopped and spoke to her. She certainly was pretty enough to figure in any film. The simile of a peach which has now become a slang expression seemed singularly appropriate when applied to her. Her cheeks were really peach-like, and so was the shape of her face, with bright eyes that almost disappeared when she laughed. Laughter came to her easily, and her smile seemed hardly to be the expression of a passing pleasure, but the result of a permanent cast of features.

She was always beautifully dressed in a short jacket and trousers of flowered silk and brocade, with a very high collar. She wore her hair in the style of unmarried girls in Canton, parted in the middle, plastered down behind her ears, and with a silk braid at the end of her long pigtail. Being a rich man's daughter, she wore bracelets and ear-rings of green jade from Yunnan.

Kuniang had always a lot to say about The Little Moon. From her I learnt that Yur had many foreign friends in Peking. She used to frequent the cosmopolitan society of the Legations, the Customs, and the banks, and was much in request at missionary tea-parties. What pleasure she got out of it all, I do not know, for she knew only three or four phrases of pidgin-English, and the foreigners who could converse with her in her own language were few. But I have noticed that the Chinese who come to foreigners' teas and receptions are quite content to sit about and say nothing. They seem to find us amusing to watch. On the other hand, Yur's foreign acquaintances treated her less as a friend than as an attractive piece of local colour.

A greater intimacy was attempted by the student-interpreters of the Legations and by juniors of the Customs Service. These young men doubtless imagined that it might be pleasanter to practise the Chinese language with a sixteen-year-old girl than to study the twenty-four examples of filial piety with a teacher. They endeavoured, on various occasions, to indulge in a mild flirtation with Yur. But sentimental excursions into *le pays du tendre*, as practised in the West, did not form part (at least in those days) of a Chinese girl's social accomplishments. More than one young man who tried to express affection for The Little Moon in well-chosen phrases retired discomfited and nonplussed by her disconcerting habit of calling a spade a spade.

An ancient euphemism – the 'lily feet' – describes the fashionably bound feet of the Chinese women. The custom, which is now dying out, was always more prevalent in the south than in the north. Yur, born and bred in Canton, had tiny feet by nature, made smaller by artificial deformation.

One should not mention a lady's feet in China. They are not a fit subject for conversation among nice-minded people (was not a similar reticence once prevalent with us respecting the Queen of Spain's legs?). But Yur had to accustom herself to such lapses from propriety in the talk of her Western friends. The wonder of her butterfly feet never failed to arouse pity and astonishment. The sole of her pointed shoe measured, on the outside, less than five inches. She could not walk more than a few steps at a time. But this privation cast no shadow over her natural good humour.

I asked Kuniang how Yur's 'lily feet' would go down on the film. She seemed to think that they would not matter, though presumably Cocachin was not Chinese at all, but a Mongol, and her feet would have been like any one else's.

'But Fédor has given up the Marco Polo idea now. He is painting a portrait of Yur in a cuirass and plumed helmet, something like Father Castiglione's picture of Ch'ien Lung's famous "Perfumed Concubine".'

'How does Mr. Su like the idea of his daughter being painted in the guise of an imperial concubine?'

'He is very proud. He thinks it a great compliment.'

One day Kuniang told me that Yur was engaged to be married. The bridegroom was the Ambàn of Cherchen, that is to say, Chinese Commissioner in Sin-kiang, beyond Mongolia and north of Tibet. The Ambàn had shown great kindness to the agent of the bank, who had been sent to explore his almost unknown province. They had agreed to intensify existing business relations and to foster trade with the outer world through the agencies of the bank in North China. Among the commodities that the Ambàn desired to import was a wife from Peking. What could be more natural than to send him the comprador's daughter?

Before leaving for the bridegroom's country, Yur made a round of farewell calls on her European and American friends. All were profuse in their congratulations, and some of them gave her wedding presents. The manager of the Russian Bank and his wife gave her a gramophone and one hundred records, chosen with discrimination and musical taste. They ranged from 'Sonny Boy' to the Ride of the Valkyrie, and from 'La petite Tonquinoise' to 'O che gelida manino' out of La Bohème. The principal and teachers of the American Mission School gave her a dressing-case with all the fittings necessary for a Western lady's toilet. Yur appeared much pleased with these gifts, which would certainly raise her in the estimation of the Ambàn, her future husband. I forgot to say that Kuniang gave her a picnic basket, with Thermos flask and other gadgets. We bought it together at Moyler and Powell's in Morrison Street.

To many people it appeared doubtful whether it really could be an enviable fate for a girl, accustomed since childhood to all the luxuries obtainable in Canton and in Peking, to wed the Ambàn of a remote province in

Central Asia. But whatever Yur's feelings on the subject, she continued, as ever, to smile. The prospect of
setting forth on a two months' journey over deserts of
shifting sand and waterless tracts of black gravel, to
seek a bridegroom whom she had never seen, apparently
did not displease her. And as long as she was satisfied
there was no more to be said.

She left Peking at the end of September, by the train
that goes to Ta Tung Fu (on the Kalgan line), whence she
was to proceed by caravan.

In spite of the early morning hour, many of Yur's
friends gathered at the station to say good-bye, and to
offer boxes of sweets and flowers.

Kuniang naturally wanted to go to the station, and I
took it upon myself to accompany her. The Kalgan line
has its terminus outside the Hsi-chi-men, at the opposite
end of the town from where we live. We arrived there
only two minutes before the train started. Mr. Su, who
greeted us with effusion, was to accompany his daughter
as far as Ta Tung Fu. He was standing on the platform,
smiling like a jovial Buddha, among a crowd of festive
relations. Yur was sitting in a corner seat of the railway
carriage, with the door open on to the platform (there
are no corridor cars on that line). She was smiling as
usual, as she accepted the good wishes that were
proffered her by her friends, who crowded round with
smiles and little bows. Yur had driven to the station in a
motor, but it had been necessary to cross the platform
on foot – no light undertaking for her. Although about to
start on a journey really worthy of Marco Polo, she was
dressed in pale blue brocade. Her hair was done up as if
she were already a married woman, with a black band
across her forehead to hold a big round pearl. Her fingers were covered with rings, her feet encased in tiny
pink shoes – the colour of good fortune – embroidered
with five bats, emblems of the Five Felicities.

After much ringing of bells and blowing of whistles,
the train moved off, while on the platform friends and

relations waved their handkerchiefs and through the window of the receding car Yur smiled at them for the last time, showing the two rows of her pearly teeth.

Four months later we received, in Peking, the news of her death.

It had occurred on the journey, when she was within two weeks of her destination.

The first rumour of the tragedy reached me when I had gone to the library of the Peking Club, to change some books. I was much distressed and felt that I would have to break the news to Kuniang. Before doing so I had better make certain that it was true. So I went round to the Russian Bank, in Legation Street, and asked for Mr. Su, wondering if he would be in his office. I was told that he was, and that he would receive me in a few minutes. I asked a clerk if the news about Yur was confirmed and he said, Yes, there could be no doubt, and no hope.

Mr. Su received me in his office on the first floor, a fine room upholstered in green leather, with old French prints on the walls. As I entered, Mr. Su rose from his big writing-table, replacing the telephone receiver on its stand. He was richly dressed in plum silk brocade and seemed very little moved by his sad loss. His face wore the smile prescribed by Chinese etiquette when receiving visitors, even those who come to condole. My expressions of sympathy were met with no less suitable expressions of gratitude. Mr. Su offered me a seat in one of his comfortable arm-chairs, passed me a box of Russian cigarettes, and began to tell me how the misfortune had occurred, or at least how he imagined it must have occurred.

Poor little Yur's caravan had lost its way – so it appeared – after passing the borders of Mongolia and while crossing the desert of Lob. Mr. Su could not say for certain what had caused the disaster; similar tragedies occur frequently in those regions and are brought about by sandstorms, sudden falls in the temperature, lack of sufficient provisions, accidents to camels and to mules, or by a combination of such circumstances.

According to Mr. Su, the caravan started across the desert with ten camels and five ponies. Yur's escort consisted of two Manchu women, four menservants, and an adequate number of camel-drivers. It was not known how the baggage and provisions had been distributed, nor if the gramophone and other wedding presents had reached thus far. Mr. Su touched on various hypotheses as to what might have happened. He spoke in terms that any Westerner might have used, supposing him well posted in the matter of caravan travel through the deserts of Central Asia. I was surprised when he added, as if it were the most natural thing in the world:

'I had provided her also with a sword of peach wood.'

'A sword of peach wood! What for?'

'To keep off the evil spirits.'

I made no comment, but my face must have betrayed a certain scepticism, for Mr. Su added:

'You think me superstitious. Yet even Western travellers know of the existence of evil spirits in the desert, and many have heard their voices. You do not believe me?'

'It all depends on what you mean by evil spirits.'

'I would not attempt to define them, but if you will wait here a moment I will bring some books from our library.'

He left the room and came back after a few minutes, carrying two books, one of which he handed to me, pointing to the open page where he wished me to read. It was the first volume of Colonel Yule's *Cathay and the Way Thither*, containing the story told by the Blessed Odoric of Pordenone to his companion, Friar Marchesino da Bassano, about a valley where he saw 'dead bodies lying'. These were the victims of an evil spirit living in the rocks and from whom the narrator escaped only by making the sign of the Cross while repeating *Verbum caro factum est.* . . .

'And I heard therein sundry kinds of music, but chiefly nakers which were marvellously played upon.'

In his commentary, Colonel Yule mentioned the solemn passage in which Our Lord Himself adopted the Jewish phraseology in this matter (Luke xi. 24): 'When the unclean spirit is gone out of a man, he walketh through dry places, seeking rest.'

'You see!' exclaimed Mr. Su. 'Mine is no superstition. It is even a matter of Christian faith. But if you want further proof, you will find it in the Book of Messer Marco Polo, where he speaks of the very desert where Yur was lost.'

He handed me the book and showed me the page where the Venetian traveller describes the desert of Lob, as it was in the thirteenth century, and as it is still. I knew the passage already and glanced at it only to please Mr. Su.

As Marco Polo says, the length of the desert is so great that it would take a year or more to ride from one end of it to the other, and where its breadth is least, it takes a month to cross. Pools of brackish water are to be found every two or three days, but hardly sufficient for a large caravan. There are no animals. There is nothing for them to eat:

'A marvellous thing is related of this desert. When travellers move by night and one of them lags behind or chances to fall asleep, when he tries to rejoin his company, he will hear spirits talking and will suppose them to be his comrades. Sometimes the spirits will call him by name. Thus shall a traveller be led astray, so that he never finds his party. In this way many have perished. Sometimes you shall hear a variety of musical instruments, and sometimes the sound of drums.'

Mr. Su watched me read. He did not give the impression of being stricken with grief for the loss of a beloved daughter. Indeed, his manner betrayed a certain satisfaction at being able to air his knowledge. With a slight feeling of aversion, I rose to depart and did not trouble to repeat my condolences. Mr. Su accompanied me, still smiling, to the door.

I could have given him the explanation of Marco Polo's narrative. I had it from an English explorer, Major Dalrymple Bruce, who in 1907 accomplished the overland journey from Simla to Peking. He wrote a book about it, which he appropriately called In the Footsteps of Marco Polo.

The voices are heard in winter, which in those latitudes means the greater part of the year. Along the borders of the marshes, such as those of Kara Koshun, you will hear, when you camp for the night, the sounds of musical instruments and of drums. They are nothing else than the groaning and the thunder of the floes, as the temperature drops and the ice freezes harder.

Such are the Voices in the Desert. But the problem of how Yur met her death still remains unsolved.

It is no deep mystery. Tales of travel across the deserts of Central Asia, on the beds of dried-up seas, tell of the inevitable dearth of food for man and beast. They describe the sufferings of the horses, obliged to toil heavily on a pound of corn a day. They tell of the difficulty of finding water and protection from the terrible north wind.

Any small accident – the loss of a case of food; a fallen pony, a lame camel – may endanger the whole caravan.

The Ambàn of Cherchen had not gone himself, nor had he sent any one to meet his bride. Wives are easy to come by. No great harm if one gets lost by the way.

Yur's caravan was not a big one. Danger must have come upon them, in what form we do not know. But once the blow had fallen, it is not difficult to imagine the rest. The women-servants, being Manchus, had not the 'lily feet' of the Chinese girl. It is not probable that they, or the camel-drivers, when their lives hung in the balance, gave a thought to The Little Moon. For them escape might yet be possible. A girl who could only take a few steps at a time was doomed.

The last scene in the tragedy is easy to conjure up:

Night falling on the frozen marshes. A small, slim figure in the starry solitude, the old fixed smile on her lips and the fear of death in her eyes, trying every now and then to advance on tiny blood-stained feet. And in answer to her cries for help the mocking voices of the desert. . . .

'. . . and he will hear spirits talking, and will suppose them to be his comrades.'

15   Letters From My Temple

SAN SHAN YUR
16th June

I have rented a temple in the Western Hills, to go there
for week-ends, and perhaps for an occasional fortnight
in the autumn or the spring. It is about eighteen miles
from Peking, and one can reach the place easily enough
on horseback. Also one can go most of the way by motor,
along the new road that branches off to the Summer
Palace.

The train that goes to Men-to-kou, on the other side of
the mountains, stops at a little station two miles distant
from the village of Pa-ta-chu. This name means 'The Hill
of the Eight Sanctuaries'. My temple is one of the eight
that mount up the hill-side among the oaks, the maples,
and the stunted pines. Both temples and trees nestle in
the hollows, where they are protected from the north
wind, which keeps the hill-tops shorn of vegetation.

The word 'temple' comes from the Greek $\tau\acute{\epsilon}\mu\nu\epsilon\iota\nu$,
which means 'to cut out, to separate, to isolate', alluding
to the exclusive character of that which is sacred to the
gods. But Chinese gods, though sometimes fierce and
terrifying, are not exclusive. They like company and are
not particular what company they keep.

Also, one must bear in mind the Oriental idea of a
sacred mountain (there are five of them in China, not
including Pa-ta-chu). To the faithful who visit these holy
places, the 'temple' is not one or the other of the

sanctuaries that are built up the hill-side, but the hill itself. When worshipping the deities, to whom they pray at Pa-ta-chu, human beings merely add their devotions to those of nature. The pilgrim burns incense and makes his vows on the altar of Buddha, while all around him the birds, the mountain streams, and the flowering shrubs do likewise. As R.F. Johnston explains, in his *Buddhist China*, a sacred mountain, or an island, is only a great altar raised to the Buddha, and the sky is its jewelled dome.

The same idea can be found in Carducci's *Canto dell' Amore* (the Song of Love, which is not a love song!), where he speaks of the paean of adoration that rises from the tender green of budding corn, from farms and vine-yards on brown hill-sides, from silvery lakes and winding rivers: one chant in the echo of a thousand songs; one hymn in the murmur of a thousand prayers:

Salute, o genti umane affaticate,
Tutto trapassa e nulla può morir.
Noi troppo odiammo e sofferimmo. Amate!
Il mondo è bello e sacro è l'avvenir![1]

At my temple, in summer-time, the cicadas take the principal part in the chorus. And a fine noise they make! They are of many different kinds, and there is one kind that produces a strident metallic sound, something between the rasp of a file and the twang of a jews' harp. It dies off in a whir, like an alarum-clock that runs down. His song, so I am told, serves the gentleman cicada as a sexual call. He keeps it up for a long time. I sometimes wish the lady would respond sooner. This and other noises serve to augment the impression of a more than tropical heat. Frogs croak, day and night, in the pond where the lotus grows. Hoopoes and larks, ravens and magpies, all join in the concert of sacred music.

[1] Hail O tiréd human people. Everything passes. Nothing ever dies.
Too much have we hated and suffered. Love, then!
The world is beautiful and the future sacred.

My temple is called the San Shan Yur, which means the 'Temple of the Three Mountains', just as in Rome there is a Trinità dei Monti.

I pay a rent of thirty silver taels a month, a sum that recalls the betrayal of Judas. But one must not think badly of the two old priests, who act as caretakers, if they have sold something sacred to an unbeliever. It is true that I have acquired the right to occupy some of the pavilions. But all over Asia temples are open to those who seek shelter.

Despite my presence here, Chinese pilgrims still make their way up the stone-flagged path to the temple door, and burn incense before the image of the Buddha. I am glad that they should do so. When they meet me, they bow and smile delightedly, as if I were one of the sights. Perhaps I am.

But I wish that the itinerant vendors were less numerous. It is the pride of Peking housewives that everything can be bought at their own door. One might almost say the same of my temple. The travelling merchants come at all hours, carrying their wares in baskets, suspended at either end of a long pole of split bamboo, which rests on the shoulder of the bearer. It must be hard work, climbing up these steep mountain paths with a heavy burden, especially if they have come all the way from Peking.

What they sell is generally something to eat, little cakes and candied fruit and pasties, steamed bread (man-tu) and fried bean-curd. Others offer tobacco or sweets. Sometimes they are barbers, hoping to find among country rustics men who still shave their heads and have pigtails to plait and trim. One man mends broken pots and pans, and even porcelain (by means of little copper fasteners); he has a tiny gong in his outfit, which he sounds as he walks along.

These poor people arrive here hot and weary from the long tramp, and they take their rest in the first courtyard of the temple, sitting there by the hour, talking to

212

the two priests or to my servants. And they spit and spit and spit, with a rasp like a rusty railway car putting on the brakes. I could never have imagined it was possible to produce such penetrating sounds by means of expectoration.

SAN SHAN YUR
10th August

This morning early I rode out from Peking, and on leaving the town I found the gates closed at the level-crossing just outside the Hsi-chi-men. To the left of the road, before you reach the railway line, is the entrance to a large temple, dedicated – so I am told – to the moon. I have also been told (my information on this matter is entirely second-hand) that the said temple is alternatively dedicated, by a certain class of foreign residents, to the pursuit of illicit love affairs. I have never been inside, but I have named it, on my own account, the Temple of Ten Thousand Smells.

Life in China is a liberal education in the matter of smells. This morning while waiting in the serried crowd of ponies, carts, rickshaws, and pedestrians, I amused myself by analysing, as far as I was able, the aroma which arose from that compact agglomeration of human beings. There was a funeral procession which the closing of the gates had cut in two. The deceased was on my side of the level-crossing, and my olfactory organs informed me that he (or she) must have waited a long time for an 'auspicious day' suitable for the burial. Two carts stood near by, full of the residue of beetroot that had been used in a sugar refinery; also several other carts with sides made of basket-work, transporting manure, best described with *le mot de Cambronne*. There is a saying that 'half the population of China finds occupation in transporting the excrements of the other half'. The breath of the rickshaw coolies illustrated the well-known fact that garlic provides the motive power for rickshaws, as petrol for motor-cars. From the neighbouring restaurants, the languid breeze brought the effluvia of kitchens where both fish and pig were being fried in sesamum oil. I may add that these odours, and others that I could not trace to their first cause, did not represent a temporary bouquet. They are endemic in that locality. In the case of the inhabitants, possibly habit has blunted the senses, but unless a north wind is blowing, casual visitors had best not tarry near the Temple of the Moon.

The level-crossing this morning was closed, not because we were waiting for a train to go by, but for a train to be moved out of the way. In shunting the carriages of the Peking-Kalgan express (so-called), they had left them standing for an indefinite period, a quarter of a mile outside the Hsi Chi Men station and right across the road that leads to Men-to-kou and the Western Hills. Patience is a virtue in which the Chinese excel. Of all the crowd that waited there, I was the only one who obviously chafed at delay.

As my pony was restless and there seemed to be no prospect of continuing on our way, I dismounted and handed the reins to Pure Virtue. So I was able to stand a little way off and not in the thick of the crowd. I found myself next to an elderly lady with grey hair. Like me, she was waiting to cross the railway line. I guessed that she must be English or American, and, judging by the antiquated shape of her sun-helmet and the unfashionable cut of her skirt, I took her for a missionary. She was tall and slightly bent, with fine features and an expression of dignified benevolence. I was astonished to see her on foot in that smelly crowd. So few people walk in Peking, except in the Legation Quarter or on top of the Tartar Wall. Rickshaws are cheap and plentiful.

The closing of the level-crossing threatened to prolong itself indefinitely, so the lady took a book out of her satchel and began to read. She held the volume so that I could see the outer cover. What *do* you suppose she was

reading? *The Scented Garden* of the Sheikh el Nauphtal.
Nor was the antithesis only in the matter of perfumes
and of smells. The book itself, of which the lady had a
French version, was once translated into English by Sir
Richard Burton (of *Arabian Nights* fame), but the
manuscript was burnt by Lady Burton before it could
reach the publisher, because, she said, her husband's
reputation would suffer if his name were connected
with such a book.

But surely, I asked myself, a lady who read *The
Scented Garden* could hardly be a missionary? And then
I noticed, a little way off, a smart brougham of Chinese
make, all glass windows and shining lamps. Inside was a
young person whom I recognized as an inmate of 'The
White House', an establishment of ill-fame, situated on
the Austrian glacis. And then I remembered having
heard that the institution in question had recently
changed hands. Its new proprietress, so I had been told,
was an elderly matron of most dignified appearance.
The lady whom I had been observing with so much interest had found the crowd obnoxious and had got out of
her brougham to stand, like myself, a little way off. She
belonged to Mrs. Warren's profession. And I had taken
her for a missionary! What a pity it was not a Chinese
establishment that she directed! The little lady who
drove with her in the brougham was well known among
the foreign Legation Guards. Even I knew her by sight.
She was no great courtesan. In the East houses in 'the
red light district' have both dignity and prestige. The
lady who read *The Scented Garden* ought to have been
at the head of the *Wen Hwa Pan*, 'The Company of
Literature and of Flowers'. She was wasted at the White
House.

At last the train moved on, and we passed over the level-
crossing on our various errands.

The summer rains have flooded the countryside and
turned the sunken roads into ditches, deep in water. I

had to stick to the new road, which has been opened for motor traffic and is built up above the ancient level. The camels that bring coal from Men-to-kou are allowed to use this road, because their padded feet do no damage. But the heavy-wheeled, heavily burdened Chinese carts still have to struggle amid the deep ruts and the sticky mud of the old highway. It is painful to watch the unfortunate ponies and donkeys strain and slip, with heaving flanks and distended nostrils. And it outrages one's sense of justice that those who bear the heaviest burden should be condemned to use the roughest paths, while the good road is reserved for such as need it least.

My arrival at the temple was enlivened by one of those domestic incidents which lend variety to the otherwise monotonous business of housekeeping in China. Exalted Virtue, the number two cook, and a couple of coolies, had arrived before me, having accomplished the journey partly by train and partly on donkeys. They had brought provisions for two or three days. I had told them to bring corn and hay and straw for the ponies, enough for one day at least. But they had not done so, because some one had told them that everything necessary for the ponies' welfare could be bought from the farms near Pa-ta-chu. I knew that myself, but I wanted the ponies to find the stables ready for them on arrival and some *kao-liang* and hay to eat. Which they didn't. The Five Virtues always think they know better than I. Or is it the Chinaman's incorrigible gambling instinct that always prompts him to take risks?

To-day, after my arrival, a coolie had to be sent down into the plain to forage.

One can find *kao-liang* and straw almost anywhere in the country, but this does not mean that you can obtain it without delay. All the rules of etiquette, in the matter of buying and selling, have to be observed. The negotiations in the matter of fodder and bedding for my ponies must have been conducted on the following lines:

A coolie starts down the winding path towards the

plain, on foot, meditating on his own troubles. After various halts to pass the time of day with any one whom he may happen to meet on the road, he reaches the farm of some acquaintance and drops in to pay a call. Conversation begins with kind inquiries as to the health, the material prosperity, and the spiritual felicity of the household, more especially of the aged father, the venerable mother, and such other members of the elder generation as may be still alive (secondary wives of the aged father, etc.). Many graceful allusions are made to the fact that to-day (Fifteenth Day of the Seventh Moon) is the Chuan-yuan-chieh, that is to say, the Festival of the Spirits. After which, the coolie may mention, as if telling a piece of interesting gossip, that up at the San Shan Yur there is a foreign devil. Descriptions of the foreign devil follow in due course and questions concerning his name, his age, and nationality. Some confusion arises from the fact that the Italian chargé d'affaires is also occupying a temple in the vicinity. To people who have no knowledge of those who live beyond 'the Four Seas' there is little difference between In-guo-jen (English) and I-guo-jen (Italian). Therefore the farmers are convinced that the coolie is making a mistake, and they go on repeating to each other:

'In-guo-jen.'

'I-guo-jen.'

'In-guo.'

'I-guo,' till the coolie clears up the misunderstanding by furnishing particulars (according to his own conception) about the two different brands of foreign devil. After which, more questions:

'How many wives has the foreign devil got? And concubines? And sons? Is he rich? How does he earn his rice?'

And so forth and so on.

Another item of news. The foreign devil came up to the San Shan Yur riding. He keeps ponies.

Therefore it might be possible to sell him some *kaoliang*, some straw, some bran, etc., etc., etc.

Long and animated discussion as to the possible profits of such an undertaking, and calculations as to whether it would be worth while to float a company with the object of providing the foreign devil's ponies with such farm produce as they may require. The decision is favourable, and the company begins its activities with the election of a Chairman, a Treasurer, etc., etc.

The priest of the local temple is then approached with the object of ascertaining if the day be auspicious for the inauguration of the new company's undertakings. The reply being satisfactory, suitable rites are accomplished (burning of incense and payment of some small coin to the priest), after which an expedition is organized, consisting of six persons and four donkeys, entrusted with the mission of taking up straw and bran and *kao-liang* to the temple of the San Shan Yur, where my ponies had been waiting all this time to be fed.

SAN SHAN YUR
12th August

This morning I went for a ride down in the plain, which is all green with the young millet and Indian corn. I passed through the village of Pa-li-chuang, and at the foot of the great pagoda, with its thirteen tiers of sloping roofs, I saw a wretched puppy with its hind legs broken, trying to drag itself away on its front legs from some children who were tormenting it. I spurred my pony to get away from the spot. It would have been kinder to dismount and put the poor thing out of its misery with a blow on the head from the handle of my hunting-crop. But at that moment I was merely sickened with the sight, and by the puppy's helpless yelps of pain. I did not think of interfering.Now I am haunted by regret for my lack of kindness and promptitude, and I ask myself if the poor puppy is still alive and suffering?

It is odd, now I come to think of it, that the episode should have occurred just there, for there is a beggar in the village of Pa-li-chuang, whom everybody about here knows. Like the puppy he drags himself along the ground by his arms, for the sinews of his legs have been cut, and his limbs are all twisted. He will never walk again. He is a survival of the past, victim of the grim punishment that was sometimes meted out to thieves. I often see that beggar as I pass and throw him a few coppers.

On reaching my temple once more, I met some pilgrims coming out. During my absence they had visited the pavilions and offered their devotions. Incense lingered in the sunlit courtyards, and the doors of the central pavilion were open. This is not one of the buildings occupied by me, and I very rarely enter it. To-day I went in. There seemed to be a lot of rubbish littered about, not to mention some cases of vermuth and an old hip-bath. But from over the top of five sacrificial vases a gilded Buddha looked down at me through half-closed eyes.

I am not ignorant of the self-sacrifice of the Bodhisats, who refuse to attain the supreme beatitudes as long as there is sin and suffering on earth (there is no sweeter story than that of Kwan Yin, who turned back from the gates of heaven because she heard a baby cry). Yet I feel that, in most Oriental creeds, however great their appeal and profound their inspiration, there is a certain hopelessness which almost seems to justify the abstention from holding out a helping hand to those who are in danger and distress. As with the puppy this morning (and with the beggar), the only deliverance is death, and that will come in time. We who live in the East unconsciously come to accept a point of view which forms a mental characteristic of a third of the human race.

Yet despite the suffering all around him, and the fundamental pessimism of his various creeds, John Chinaman is by no means depressed. He takes life as it comes and is always ready to smile at the foreign devil's vagaries, and to laugh at scurrilous stories that were new when the world was young.

The Buddhist religion still awaits its Messiah, called Maitreya. A poem (*Anagata Vamsa*) describes the golden age that the world will enjoy when Maitreya shall appear. There are images in Tibet and in Japan, which represent him with classic features, a noble bearing, and an expression which is both gentle and serene. Not so in China.

Chinese Buddhism may be distinguished from Lamaism by the special way it represents Milo Fo, the Chinese Messiah, so different from the generally accepted idea of Maitreya. Milo Fo is a fat old gentleman, with a large bare paunch and a jovial smile. There is a statue of him here in my temple, in one of the minor pavilions up on the hill-side. Poor old divinity! The roof has fallen in, and in wet weather the rain beats down on his unprotected head and runs over his rotundities. But he smiles as if he likes it. This obese Messiah impersonates the reaction of the Chinese people to the sadness that underlies their own philosophy. As if Milo Fo were saying:

'You are right. It is a hard life. Only when our souls merge into the infinite can we pass beyond the mysteries and attain the supreme beatitude. Meanwhile, as we are here, let us make the best of it. There is still some fun to be got out of this old world of ours.'

SAN SHAN YUR
16th August

I would like to be able to express in music the impressions of a summer night at my temple. A camp-bed, complete with mosquito-net, is carried out for me on to the terrace. But I cannot say that I sleep very soundly. There is much night life on the hill-side and in the valley.

To begin with, there are the fire-flies, rising out of the woods below, and merging into the constellations above, so that, as I lie in bed, I wonder sleepily where the fire-flies end and the stars begin.

Chinese in the country do not go out willingly after they have eaten the evening rice, but sometimes I see a lantern moving along the path on the other side of the valley, and I hear the voice of some one singing as he walks (to keep the evil spirits away). There are a few lights down in the village, whence comes the barking of dogs, or the braying of a donkey. Every cock crows three times, as to St. Peter, and frogs croak in chorus round the pond of a neighbouring temple. From that same temple there comes, once in every hour, the voice of a big bronze bell. It never strikes more than once, and that single note, sounding clear and dying away in the darkness, has a weird beauty of its own, a mystic appeal like a *memento mori*.

All this would sound so well in music. Grieg would have interpreted it to perfection. The dawn, with the slow rising of morning mists and the twittering of birds in the tree-tops, is there in his *Morgenstimmung*.

An occasional discordant note spoils the symphony. One of the old priests coughs a lot at night, and both he and his companion spit often and noisily.

I have endeavoured to set down some of these sounds, in view of a future musical composition. The note of the temple bell is a deep C, in the bass. An arpeggio in G minor might render the sound of the Chinese priest clearing his throat.

SAN SHAN YUR
27th August

From the hill-tops behind Pa-ta-chu I can enjoy one of the most beautiful views in the world. The highest mountain peak can be reached only from the other side of the valley, but there is a steep hill, at the back of the San Shan Yur, which I climb every evening. From up there I can see the curve of the Western Hills which embrace

Peking and form a background to the beauties of the Summer Palace. Three pagodas rise up against the horizon from the summits of isolated heights, and the fairy-like pavilions of the Empress Tzu-hsi's domain are reflected in the waters of the Ku-ying lake.

Dotted about the slopes of the hills are strange buildings, the nature of which is not immediately apparent. An enormous circular wall, about sixty feet high and fifteen broad (at the summit) supports two richly decorated pavilions. I am told that this was the grand-stand, or 'box', from which the emperor used to watch the manoeuvres of his troops. As with many other buildings round Peking, the beauty of these pavilions is in their roofs, with coloured tiles, that rise above the morning mists and flash back the midday sun.

Other walls, mounting up the hill-side in successive parallel lines, face the plain from the steep flanks of an outlying spur. They are surmounted by towers and battlements, with narrow windows where the archers stood. These buildings are models of fortified towns in Turkestan, and were set up here for experimental purposes, in anticipation of a campaign. The Emperor Ch'ien Lung used them during autumn manoeuvres. The troops that moved up the hill to attack, and those ensconced behind the battlements, did not conduct a mimic battle. They fought in earnest, with losses on either side. The experiment seems to have been instructive. Anyway, Ch'ien Lung conquered Turkestan.

At the beginning of the summer some wicker-work armchairs were put out on the terrace, but ever since I began to sit there I have been pestered by a hornet, who is busy storing provisions in the hollow cane that supports the back of one of these chairs.

I do not know whether the hornet is preparing to lay eggs, or if she is laying up provisions for herself to consume while she hibernates during the coming winter. I have read somewhere that the males die after mating, so

I deduce that my hornet is a lady. In imitation of St. Francis, I call her Sirocchia, or 'Little Sister'. But I do not feel for her that affection that the patron saint of Assisi extended to the birds, to the fishes, and to all God's creatures.

As there are several wicker-work chairs, and they do not always remain in the same place, Sirocchia never knows which is her particular one. So she goes buzzing around (generally clasping some half-dead caterpillar) in search of the hollow cane at the back of the chair, which she has selected as her larder. She shows a great liking for apricot jam, which she finds on my breakfast table, and also for a solution of acetate of lead, which I use to poultice a swollen ankle (the result of a fall from a horse). I understand and share her liking for the apricot jam, but I fear that her passion for 'dope', in the form of acetate of lead, may lead to trouble. Sirocchia cannot read the label, 'For External Use Only', and unless she curbs her desire to imbibe the mixture (which she seeks even on my ankle) there will be no further generations of little Sirocchias to buzz round my terrace when summer comes again, next year.

There are two springs on the hill-side, and the streams that descend from them meet just a little below my temple. They form a pool among the rocks, in the shade of overhanging trees. Over these pools red and blue dragon-flies dart swiftly backwards and forwards on gauze-like wings, and cool their long bodies (or are they laying eggs?) on the surface of the water. Like me, they are lovers of the hottest sunshine.

I sometimes go and bathe in those pools, and except for the dragon-flies I am alone. I would it were otherwise. Those tall rocks and shady waters would make delightful backgrounds for pictures like *La Source*.

This afternoon I took a walk down in the plain, along the sunny road towards Pi Yung Tze, and I met two foreigners, probably missionaries and, I think, Russians, dressed in white linen, cut in a strange outlandish fashion, half priestly, half Chinese. They wore large black hats with broad brims, and their long hair fell to their shoulders. There was something Biblical about their appearance that did not seem out of place just there. Indeed, there is always something Biblical about the landscape and people in an Asiatic country. In China there is much that is reminiscent of the Book of Job.

Who would be surprised if a man, such as one of those I saw this afternoon, were to stop on some hillock outside a village, and when a small crowd had collected, were to preach to them of hope and faith and charity? Half-naked children would come running, and old men hobbling along, and young women with babies in their arms. They would ask the teacher to perform some miracle of healing, convinced that such as speak of things divine must possess the powers of a divinity.

Coming home from my walk, I went to the stables and asked if the ponies had been fed. Pure Virtue said No; he would feed them at six o'clock. I asked him: 'What is the time now?'

He answered: 'Half-past six.'

Mere matters of time have very little interest for the Oriental.

After taking a cup of tea, I climbed the hill to watch the sunset.

Half-way to the top, where the trees end and the short mountain grass begins, there is a hut, with about twenty square feet of habitable space. A half-starved mongrel cur acts as a watchdog. When he sees me he retreats up the hill-side, barking noisily. His idea is that he should warn his owners of a foreign devil's approach, while he himself retires before any possible danger. The small amount of food they give him would not justify his taking risks in their defence.

At the sound of the dog barking, the door of the hut

opens and a woman appears. She has a sullen, pock-marked face, and carries a baby in her arms. Several small children and a pig emerge from the darkness of the hut; and they all stand there, staring after me as I walk away, while the cur-dog barks from afar.

The elder of the two priests, the one with the beard, has returned to the temple after being away for a week or more. I thought he might have been to see a dentist, for he has teeth only on the right side of his head. I know another priest, in a temple near Men-to-kou, who has made himself a set of false teeth with mother-of-pearl buttons, filed down and attached to a piece of whale-bone. I cannot say that the result is satisfactory. The poor man has to take out his teeth every time he wants to speak or eat. But he can smile in them, and they must give him some pleasure, or he would not wear them. *Vanitas vanitatum, omnia vanitas!*

My little priest of the San Shan Yur has not shown so much initiative, but perhaps he is content to masticate on the right side of his mouth only. A Chinese, of course, would not say 'on the right side', or 'on the left', even speaking of his own teeth. He would say north or south, or east or west, according to the direction in which he might be facing at the time:

'I have lost all my teeth on the southern side, but my northern ones are still as good as ever!'

SAN SHAN YUR
16th September

Autumn always seems much the same, whatever country I happen to be in. Spring and summer have flowers that are characteristic of the various localities. But those golden spikes of Indian corn, drying on the roofs, how often have I seen them in the West! The red and gold of oaks and maples are the same that make autumn beautiful in the Wiener Wald and in the Valley of the Rhône.

225

The blue sky and brown earth are such as one sees in Sicily. Here in China, the same colours are repeated in the blue cotton clothes and brown skins of the peasants.

To-day I had a long talk with a priest in one of the temples higher up on the hill-side. The subject of our conversation was chestnut husks and their use for dyeing. Now that I have come home I realize that I do not know the Chinese equivalent for 'chestnut husks', nor how you say 'to dye'. Yet the priest and I understood each other perfectly. I have a friend in Peking (the Director of the Salt Gabelle) who maintains that there is no such thing as a Chinese language, and that we understand each other much as animals do. There may be something in it.

There is no feeling of loneliness at my temple in the autumn. Harvest is in full swing down in the plain, and many of these temples have outhouses where the garnered crops are stored. All day long I hear the short step of donkeys on the path, and the bells that they wear on their bridles. The boys that take cows and goats to pasture call to one another across the valley, and woodcutters are busy among the dead branches. When I go for a walk round Pa-ta-chu, I am sure of meeting some Buddhist priest in the dress that is no longer that of contemporary China, but a reminiscence of past dynasties. And priest, or woodcutter, or herdsman will stop and stare at the foreign devil. Against the background of rocks and wood and stream, they form one of those characteristic pictures, such as one sees on porcelain vases or on Chinese fans.

A fine moon to-night!

I went a stroll up the hill and it was as clear as daylight. Never has my temple seemed so beautiful. The song of the cicadas, vibrating in the cool air, is more musical now than in summer. And there are still some glow-worms, like flaming jewels, among the shrubs. I saw a fire-fly pass in front of the moon; it seemed to take some light from the silver orb and to make a thread with it across the sky, weaving a spider's web among the stars.

And how pretty are the Chinese windows, with the light shining through and showing the pattern of the wooden lattice. These windows remind me (I could not say why) of northern fairy-tales. Two children get lost in a forest and wander hand in hand till they see a tiny light shining among the shadows, far far away. . . .

The cicadas are becoming rarer as the nights get cooler. But a few still remain, to chirp in sheltered nooks on the southern slopes of the hills. They remind me of a simile of Carducci's when he compares the poet, who is growing old, to cicadas that survive in September, to sing on in sunlit corners among the Tuscan hills.

That same simile applies to those who are less in touch with the New China than with the Old. It is a great ideal, which would bring the Chinese people into line with the nations of the West. But it was the older civilization that threw over us the spell of her philosophy, of her aloofness, of her disdain.

Old customs are dying, and the ideas that inspired them. It is autumn in China.

Like cicadas in September, we live on to sing her praises in sheltered temples in the hills.

SAN SHAN YUR
16th December

I came here by rail from the Hsi-chi-men station, accomplishing the last part of the journey on foot. The train was full of prosperous-looking coal merchants, going to Men-to-kou; big men, fat and jovial and noisy. They all seemed in a very good humour and quite indifferent to the fact that the train started half an hour late. Our car was heated by means of a small stove, and one of the merchants leant against it, without being aware of the fact. His fine satin robe, lined with squirrel, got badly singed. His companions hailed the mishap with bursts of laughter.

To let out the smell of burning, I opened the carriage window. Still, the train did not seem to have any intention of starting, so I watched the little boys skating on the frozen canal. They used a wooden skate, on one foot only. Most of them found it more amusing to be pulled along by a comrade on a tiny sled, on which there was hardly room to sit down. The little boys tumbled and shouted on the ice, while the merchants chaffed one another inside the car. And the train coolie moved about with little pots of fresh tea and small spongy towels, steamed over boiling water, for the passengers to pass over their faces and hands.

An hour later, when I got out of the train to walk over the fields towards Pa-ta-chu, the sun was shining brightly on the tombs that are dotted about the plain. Strings of camels passed along the high road, proud of their winter coats. From the farmhouses came nasal voices singing, and magpies answered from the trees.

The streams are frozen near my temple, and so are the pools where I used to bathe. The little waterfalls, over the rocks, are now long shimmering icicles.

On arriving at the temple I found a great commotion going on. It appears that during my absence an old overcoat of mine, which had been left there, has disappeared. The priests disclaim any knowledge of it. They suggest that we should consult a seer. He would describe the person who took the coat away. Isn't there something in the first Book of Samuel, about Saul consulting a seer, when the she-asses belonging to his father got lost? In China the seer has a boy with him (he must be virgin) whom he puts into a kind of trance. The boy looks into a bowl of water and tells what he sees there. I left Exalted Virtue and the priests to fight it out among themselves.

A large iron stove has been put into the so-called

'guest-room', where I now sleep and read and eat. Even in the house I go about with a leather jacket lined with sheepskin and with a fur cap pulled over my ears. Though I do manage to get some hot water for a tub, the towels are stiff and crackly with ice. Outside, the thermometer marks sixteen below zero, and to-night it will be colder still. Window-panes of rice-paper may be fairy-like, but they don't keep out the cold. The elder of the two priests coughs more than usual. I wonder if he will get through the winter?

I climbed the usual hill, and the usual dog came out to bark at me, followed by the woman with the pock-marked face and her baby in her arms. The smaller children stood beside her, holding on to her trousers and repeating: 'Ba, ba, ba, ba . . .' like an echo of the dog's barking. The usual pig was there, too, a little farther up the hill-side. He was rooting for something to eat among the frozen grasses. High up in the sky a great hawk circled over our heads. And it seemed to me that the hawk and the pig talked to one another in the silence of the wintry hills:

The Hawk. 'Here comes the usual foreign devil.'

The Pig. 'Yes. He is not dead yet.'

The Hawk. 'Worse luck! I always hope he may have a fall, down there by the grey rocks. The spring is frozen and the ground slippery with ice. A false step or a sudden gust of wind might do the trick. After a night like this on the mountain-side, he would make a good meal for you and me.'

The Pig. 'The peasants would find him; those who live in the hut.'

The Hawk. 'Even if they did, they would not help him, for fear of being accused of having caused his fall.'

The Pig. 'Would one night be sufficient to kill him?'

The Hawk. 'Yes, if he had a broken leg, to keep him still. The crows tell me that every night some one dies in the streets of Peking.'

At this point the hawk flew away towards the plain. I could follow his flight only for a moment: a speck of gold in the sunlight above the purple hills. Then he vanished.

The pig looked at me discontentedly and grunted.

16 Again Kuniang's Diary

The following are a few extracts from Kuniang's diary after two years of married life:

Fifteenth Day of the Eighth Moon
  Chung-ch'iu-chieh: 'Mid-autumn festival.'
  Little Chink has a sand-heap in the garden. The sand was brought all the way from Shan-hai-kwàn. The amah is very proud of that sand-heap. No child in this part of Peking can boast of anything so grand. As to-day is a great holiday (a sort of harvest festival), Little Chink had a party and other babies were invited to play on the sand-heap. They came escorted by their amahs, and our amah acquired 'face'.
  Little Lu came to see us to-day. He was wearing a suit of Shantung silk, cut foreign fashion, and patent-leather shoes, which must be uncomfortable in this warm weather. But they certainly were very shiny. I understand that Little Lu is thinking of getting married. Then his mother's prestige will be even greater, especially if he has children. *Epouse et mère, ce sont les épaulettes. Grandmère, c'est le bâton de maréchal!*

Twenty-seventh Day of the Eighth Moon
  Sheng-tan-chieh: 'Birthday of Confucius.'
  This last week has reminded me of old days, and I have had no time to write up my diary.
  Since Tuesday last, Fédor and Natasha have been staying with us. The roof of their house was in a bad

231

state and the summer rains flooded them out. Patushka and Matushka have taken refuge in a Chinese hotel, for to have workmen in the house in Peking is the very devil. They spit all over the place, and the smell of garlic almost knocks you down.

King Cophetua heard about it from Exalted Virtue, who brings him all the gossip. If he had guessed what the outcome would be, Exalted Virtue would not have mentioned the matter. For King Cophetua suggested that the young people should come and stay with us. I think he wants to show that he does not disapprove of them as he used to.

Fédor and Natasha promised me to be on their best behaviour. They are grateful for being asked, as their rain-sodden house, full of workmen, is uncomfortable and depressing. So far everything has gone well. They play with Little Chink, to his vast delight, and their deportment might grace an embassy. I wonder how long it will be before they show the cloven hoof?

Twenty-eighth Day of the Eighth Moon

We have suddenly discovered that Fédor has been painting the walls of the bathroom in the guests' pavilion. He said something about doing so, I believe, to King Cophetua, who paid no attention. Taking silence for consent, Fédor has now finished two wonderful frescoes, one of Susannah and the elders, and one of Leda and the swan. The figures and backgrounds are Chinese.

Neither King Cophetua nor I have anything to complain of, but the Five Virtues, who miss the Biblical and classical allusions, are so shocked that we can hardly get them to tidy up that bathroom any more.

First Day of the Ninth Moon

Two or three nights ago, at dinner, I happened to mention that the door of the pavilion, where King Cophetua has his study, was badly lighted on the outside, and I suggested that a Chinese lantern (or two) might be hung there, with an electric bulb inside. A long discussion followed about Chinese lanterns generally and horn lanterns in particular.

The next day Fédor and Natasha went off to the fair at the Loong-fu Ssèu, and returned later in triumph with two lanterns of the kind that were once carried in the street in front of some important person's palanquin.

King Cophetua expressed our common gratitude and gave orders that both the lanterns should be set up at his study door. For some reason that at first was not apparent, his orders were not carried out. Indeed, he had to repeat them several times before the lanterns were set up.

And this morning the storm burst!

Mr. Tang came, as usual, to give King Cophetua a Chinese lesson, and seeing the lanterns at the door, he stopped to read the characters that were written on them. The next moment, he rushed in to King Cophetua and asked that the lanterns be taken down *kwi-kwi*! I happened to be there, so we all came out and looked at the object of Mr. Tang's indignation.

It appears that the lanterns had once belonged to a most immoral establishment that had flourished in the days of the Empire and was suppressed not long ago. The two inscriptions were identical; they ran as follows:

'Admire the beautiful shapes and moon-like countenances of the Perfumed Boys, in the Garden of Ten Thousand Pleasures, in the Quarter of the Eight Big Hutungs!'

The lanterns were taken down again.

Fédor swears that he had no idea what the characters meant.

I wonder.

Third Day of the Ninth Moon

Yesterday I was not feeling well and went to bed soon after lunch. In the evening, Exalted Virtue brought me a tray with soup and an apple and some fried raisins. These are little pancakes of raisins cooked in batter, and very good. Ocean of Virtue got the receipt from some other cook while we were at Shan-hai-kwàn and he always sends them up now, when he wants to tempt my appetite. Exalted Virtue had a very long face when he brought me my supper. I am sure he wanted me to notice it and to ask him what was the matter. But I knew perfectly well what the matter was. He had something to say about Fédor and Natasha. He hates their being in the house and considers that we lose face by having them to stay with us.

I expected King Cophetua to come in and see me after dinner, but it was half-past ten before he turned up. He had some papers in his hand, which he laid on the dressing-table.

'How did the dinner go?' I asked. 'Did Fédor and Natasha behave themselves?'

He smiled and crossed the room, to sit on the bed beside me.

'The dinner went off all right,' he said. 'But those two young friends of yours are *the* most disgraceful young criminals I have ever seen.'

'What have they done now?'

'Something that will please you very much. They have extorted from me an order for Fédor to paint a portrait of you and Little Chink.'

'How perfectly lovely! I always wanted a portrait of Little Chink. How did they succeed in persuading you?'

'Sheer blackmail!'

'What *do* you mean?'

'Well, Natasha went to their house this afternoon and brought back some portfolios and some drawings of Fédor's. She took advantage of your not being there, to show them to me after dinner. They are the studies he did of you with nothing on but a smile.'

'You don't mind? Do you?' I asked anxiously.

King Cophetua laughed.

'It would be a bit late to mind anything that happened in the old days, when you went to the Russian family. But those two young fiends counted on my preferring to own the sketches myself, and not have them shown at some exhibit of Fédor's works. So he offered them to me, if I would give him a commission for a portrait. I had to accept. In fairness to Fédor I must say that it will probably be quite a good portrait and I will not get the worst of the bargain.'

I asked: 'Are those the sketches, on the dressing-table?'

'Yes. I have got the whole collection. I bet he intimidated you into posing for him, at the time.'

'He did. But I did not mind, after the first half-hour.'

'Well, here is the result. You can look at them while I undress. They will remind you of old times!'

There was a twinkle in his eye, as he laid the loose sheets beside me on the counterpane and went off through the door into his dressing-room.

Certainly the sketches are good. But I never realized how often I had posed for Fédor: almost from every angle. The prettiest study was one done at the swimming-pool, with arms uplifted to throw an india-rubber ball into the water. In another, I was sitting on a stool, with my bent knee uplifted and wonderfully foreshortened. I am pulling my last garment over my head; my face hidden, all but the mouth and chin. I remember Fédor calling out to me to stop like that. The pose was a novel one.

I am glad to have these sketches. And it is nice to know that King Cophetua doesn't mind. I told him once that Fédor wanted to paint me in the altogether and that it was difficult to refuse. I did not say that many sketches had been done. As usual, I was afraid he would write to Papà.

While I looked at the drawings, I could hear King Cophetua in his dressing-room, chuckling to himself. It is lucky that he has a sense of humour!

Fourth Day of the Ninth Moon

Fédor has lost no time in getting a canvas and starting on the portrait. To-day he made me and Little Chink sit for him in the garden, just to sketch in the figures and decide on the composition. The background is to be of the kaki-trees, with their big golden fruit among the green foliage, like the oranges in Botticelli's 'Spring' (or so Fédor says).

Fédor and Natasha are going home to-morrow, and he wants Little Chink and me to come and 'sit' there, as he says the light is better.

This time it is Little Chink who is to be in the altogether, and not I. It is my idea, for I want the portrait to show the birthmark on his shoulder, the half-moon, that I have on my forehead.

I asked Fédor if he would put in Uncle Podger. But he says No: it would hardly be fair to us. He will do a separate portrait of Uncle Podger on a red lacquer throne, with a ceremonial umbrella held over him by court eunuchs in embroidered robes.

Ninth Day of the Ninth Moon

Chung-yang-jih: 'The Festival of the "heavy" sun.'

I have been going to the Russian family's house to sit for Fédor. So has Little Chink (if you can call what he does 'sitting'). The portrait is going to be very fine. Figures, faces and background are a little indistinct, as if seen through a gentle haze of light. Little Chink looks a perfect pet. He is sitting on my knee and there is a faint halo of light behind us, like the halo that some painters put round the Virgin and infant Christ. I never thought that a portrait of me could be so beautiful and still look like me. And to think that it is Fédor who is painting it! It reminds me a little of the descriptions in the *Heavenly Trousers*. King Cophetua made me out so lovely and so lovable that I still wonder if that can be me.

It was funny being in that room again, with the Laughing Buddha leering at me from the mantelpiece.

Fédor said to me, 'Undress, Kuniang. Let me do another sketch of you as in the good old days.'

I shook my head and smiled. But he insisted. 'What difference does it make?'

'There is a difference . . . in me.'

'Nonsense! I saw you bathing, this summer at Shan-hai-kwàn. Your figure is as good as ever.'

'Are you sure? Did you not guess why I was not feeling well in these last days, while you were staying with us?'

He stopped painting and stared at me.

'You are expecting another baby?'

'Yes. If I took off my clothes now, you would notice.'

Fédor looked rather chagrined. And then he did an unexpected thing (Fédor is always unexpected!). He laid down his paint-brush and came and knelt on the floor at my feet, and lifted my hands and kissed them.

'Kuniang,' he said. 'Only the old Italian masters could paint you as you should be painted. But you have been a joy and an inspiration to me ever since we were children. God bless you, little dove, and give you the happiness you deserve.'

I don't suppose I shall ever understand Fédor!

A minute later he was teasing me by saying that he had not given King Cophetua *all* the sketches that had been done of me in the nude.

'Do you remember that for several days I made you pose, while I worked in oils, and you were bending forward with a cup in your hand? The cup should have been a lamp really, a little Grecian lamp. I wanted that for a picture of you as Psyche, stealing in to see the sleeping Cupid, just before you woke him up with a drop of hot oil!'

'But there was no Cupid!'

'Yes there was. Igor posed for that.'

Fédor refused to show me the picture. I wonder if he is not making it all up? But it is true that he did make me pose, holding a tea-cup!

Twelfth Day of the Ninth Moon

King Cophetua came in to see the portrait this morning, though it is not quite finished (Fédor was not there).

He stood and looked at it and murmured in Chinese, '*How! Ting-how!* (Good! Very good!).'

And then he said, 'Do you know anything about the Chinese character *How*? It has many meanings: good and beautiful and happy and auspicious and true. Indeed, *How* corresponds to all that is best in the world. And it is interesting to see how the Chinese have worked out the ideogram that expresses this thought. What are the radicals that make up so great a meaning? They are *Nu* and *Dze*: a woman and a baby, a mother with her child. There is nothing more beautiful in the world.'

He put his arm through mine as we looked at the picture, and he added:

'All that the world holds for me of beauty and happiness is there: Kuniang and her baby. *How! Ting-how!*'

It seemed to me that the figures in the picture moved; that Little Chink held out his arms to me; that the Kuniang in the canvas smiled and her eyes grew tender.

Perhaps it was only that my own eyes were wet!

Thirteenth Day of the Ninth Moon

This afternoon the amah went off on a pilgrimage to the Temple of the Five White Clouds, on the way to Pao-ma-chang. As she did not get back till late, I gave Little Chink his bath. King Cophetua came in and assisted at the ceremony. But I could see that he had something on his mind, and before long it came out.

'Do you know that young man in the Tientsin Book Store?' he asked.

'The shop in the Rue Marco Polo? The young man with the moustache?'

'Yes. Well, I was in there to-day, and he told me a curious thing. He said that Exalted Virtue had been inquiring after books.'

'What kind of books?'

'My books. He wanted to know if I made any money out of them.'

I was so astonished that for a moment I took my eyes off Little Chink, who made a grab at the soap and almost shot out of the bath.

'What can Exalted Virtue be up to now?' I wondered.

'It is quite obvious, I think. The Five Virtues have an idea that I write books, and that money changes hands somewhere. They feel entitled to their squeeze.'

King Cophetua and I looked into each other's eyes and laughed. But I will be very much surprised if the Five Virtues don't get that squeeze out of us somehow, some day.

First Day of the Tenth Moon

The house has been very quiet since Fédor and Natasha went home. And the Five Virtues are openly jubilant. For sheer, unrelenting enmity you cannot beat the Chinese. They enjoy it so!

Though we are in November, the weather is clear and sunny. To-day King Cophetua and I took lunch on the veranda. Little Chink was sitting on the steps near by, also lunching. That is to say, he was having mashed potatoes ladled into him by the amah.

Uncle Podger was eyeing some sparrows that were pecking round our feet for crumbs. Possibly he felt that he ought to do something about chasing them away, but it was too much trouble. We do not mention Uncle Podger's age, but he is getting very stiff in the joints and his eyes are rheumy.

King Cophetua and I must have been thinking the same thoughts, for he looked at Uncle Podger and said:

'When Ten Thousand Years have passed – you know what I mean – we will set up a sepulchral stele, with his good deeds engraved on it in Chinese and Mongol characters. And we will burn lots of incense.'

'The steam from a nice pork chop might be more acceptable. And what are his good deeds anyway?'

'Are they not written in the Book of the Heavenly Trousers? He helped to bring us together.'

'Shall we say that he made things move a bit quicker along their appointed course? And he has offered moral support at moments when we needed it badly. As you say, he shall have a marble stele all to himself, resting on the back of a monumental tortoise in a little pavilion of its own, open at the sides and with tiled eaves.'

At this point, Uncle Podger moved leisurely down the veranda steps and disappeared into the bushes. Did he find our conversation tactless?

Yet we spoke of him as within the Forbidden City they spoke of the Son of Heaven:

'Lord of Ten Thousand Years!'

THE END